John Taven

THE PROTECTING VEIL

for cello and string orchestra

CHESTER MUSIC
(a division of Music Sales Ltd)
8/9 Frith Street, London WlV 5TZ
Exclusive distributor: Music Sales Ltd,
Newmarket Road, Bury St Edmunds, Suffolk, IP33 3YB

COMPOSER'S NOTE

The Feast of the Protecting Veil of the Mother of God was instituted by the Orthodox Church to commemorate Her appearance in the church at Vlacherni (Constantinople), in the early tenth century, possibly A.D. 902. At a time of grave danger for the Greeks from Saracen invasion, Andrew, the holy fool, and his disciple Epiphanios saw the Mother of God during an all-night vigil. She was high above them in the air, surrounded by a host of saints, praying earnestly and spreading out her veil (or stole) as a protective shelter over the Christians. Heartened by this vision, the Greeks withstood the Saracen assault, and drove away the Saracen army.

It is perfectly possible to listen to *The Protecting Veil* as pure music, but it may be helpful if I recount what was in my mind during the composition. I wished to make a lyrical ikon in sound, rather than in wood, using the music of the cellist rather than a brush. The work is highly stylised, geometrically formed and meditative in character. I have tried to capture some of the almost cosmic power of the Mother of God. She is represented by the cello, and never stops singing throughout; the accompanying string music is a gigantic extension of her unending song.

The work falls into eight continuous sections, and I have made use of the eight Byzantine tones. Various Feasts were in my mind as I wrote; the second section is related to the birth of the Mother of God, the third section to the Annunciation, the fourth to the Incarnation, the fifth (which is totally unaccompanied) to her lament at the foot of the cross, the sixth to the Resurrection, the seventh to her Dormition, and the first and last sections to her cosmic beauty and power over a shattered world. The music ends with an evocation of the tears of the Mother of God.

J.T.

Born in London in 1944, **John Tavener** showed his musical talents at an early age, and by the time he entered Highgate School he was already an unusually proficient pianist and organist. He proceeded to the Royal Academy of Music where he studied with Sir Lennox Berkeley and David Lumsdaine, and won several major prizes for composition. In 1965 his dramatic cantata, *The Whale,* took the London audience by storm at its premiere given at the debut concert of the London Sinfonietta, and since that time Tavener has continued to show an originality of concept and an intensely personal idiom, making his a voice quite separate from those of his contemporaries.

Tavener's strong Christian commitment to the Orthodox Church, which he joined in 1977, has inspired all his more recent works. They include a setting of the complete Orthodox *Vigil Service, The Protecting Veil* for solo cello and strings, *Resurrection,* a large scale choral and orchestral work, *Mary of Egypt* an ikon-opera premiered at the 1992 Aldeburgh Festival, and two chamber pieces: *The Hidden Treasure* for string quartet, and *The Last Sleep of the Virgin* for string quartet and handbells.

John Tavener now lives in Sussex, but whenever possible visits Greece, where he finds the climate and peaceful atmosphere very conducive to composition.

The Protecting Veil was commissioned by the BBC for the 1989 series of Henry Wood Promenade Concerts. It is dedicated to Pamela Moody.

The first performance was given on 4th September 1989 at the Royal Albert Hall, London, by Steven Isserlis and the BBC Symphony Orchestra conducted by Oliver Knussen.

SCORING

Solo cello
Strings (minimum 8.8.6.6.3 players)

Duration: c. 42 minutes

Conductor's score, solo and orchestral parts are available on hire. The solo part is also available on sale.

This work has been recorded by Steven Isserlis and the London Symphony Orchestra conducted by Gennadi Rozhdestvensky on Virgin Classics VC 7 91474-2 (CD), and VC 7 91474-4 (cassette). The composer has made a few minor revisions to the score since this recording was issued.

THE PROTECTING VEIL

John Tavener (1987)

CH 59030

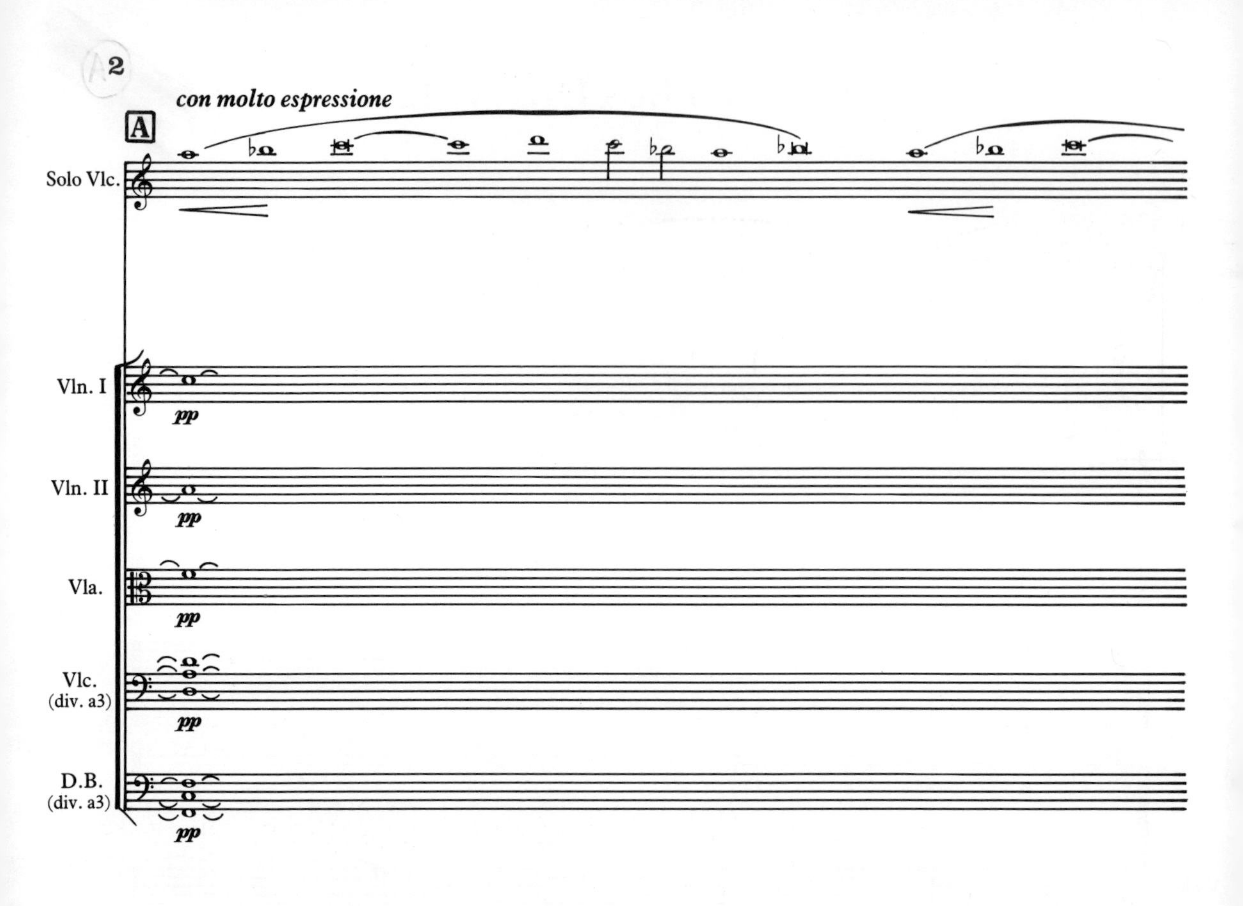
con molto espressione
A
Solo Vlc.
Vln. I
pp
Vln. II
pp
Vla.
pp
Vlc.
(div. a3)
pp
D.B.
(div. a3)
pp

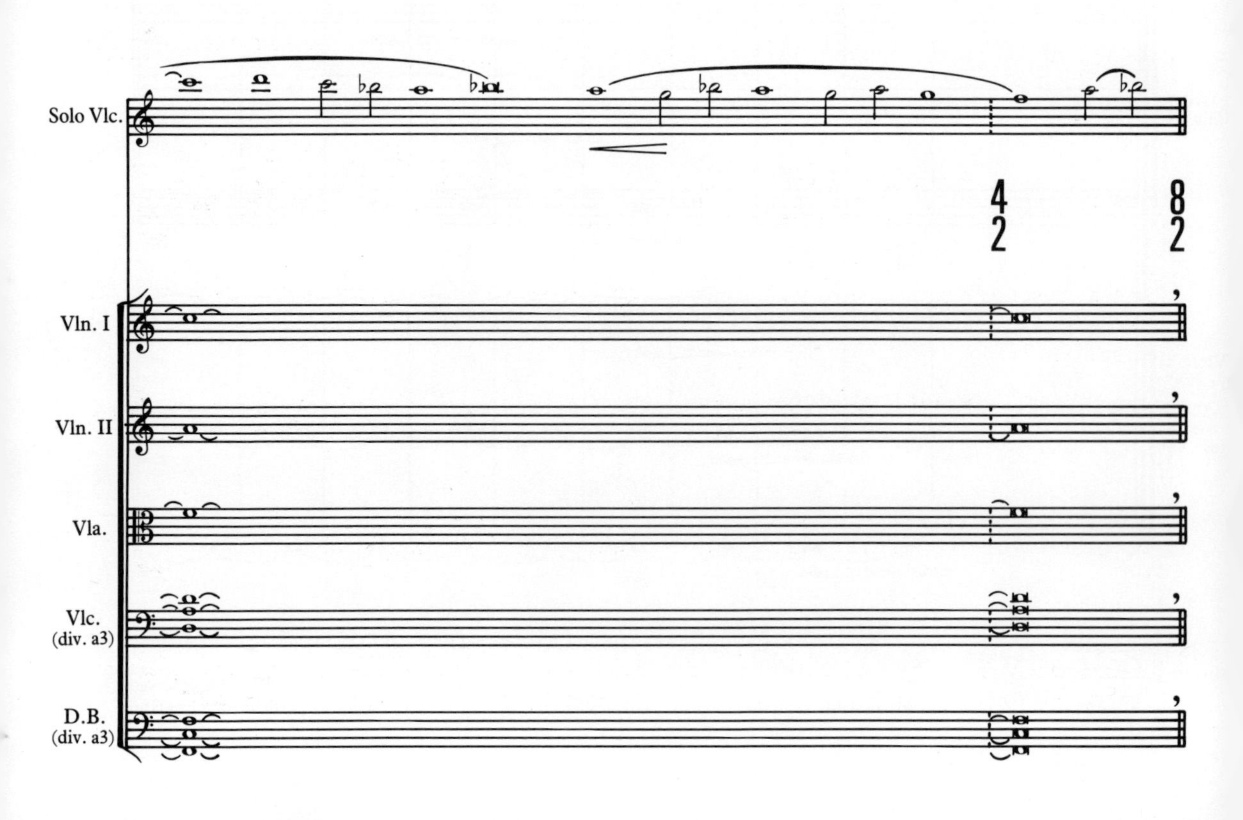
Solo Vlc.
Vln. I
Vln. II
Vla.
Vlc.
(div. a3)
D.B.
(div. a3)

B
Radiant
Solo Vlc.
sopra
8
2
6
2
8
2
4
2
p
Vln. I
(div. a2)
Vln. II
(div. a2)
Vla.
(div. a2)
Vlc.
(div. a6)
D.B.
(div. a3)

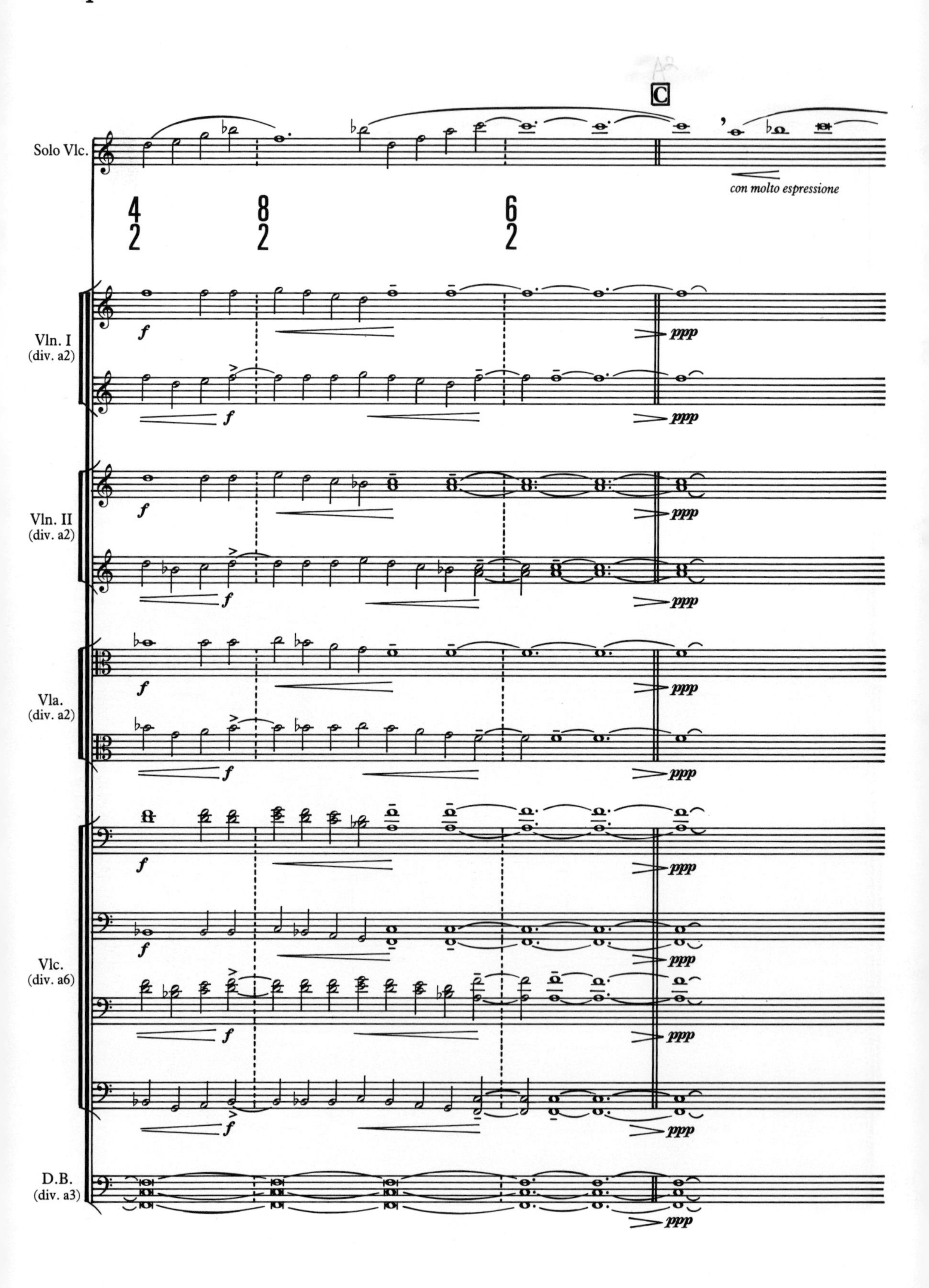
C
Solo Vlc.
con molto espressione
4 2
8 2
6 2
Vln. I (div. a2)
Vln. II (div. a2)
Vla. (div. a2)
Vlc. (div. a6)
D.B. (div. a3)
f
ppp

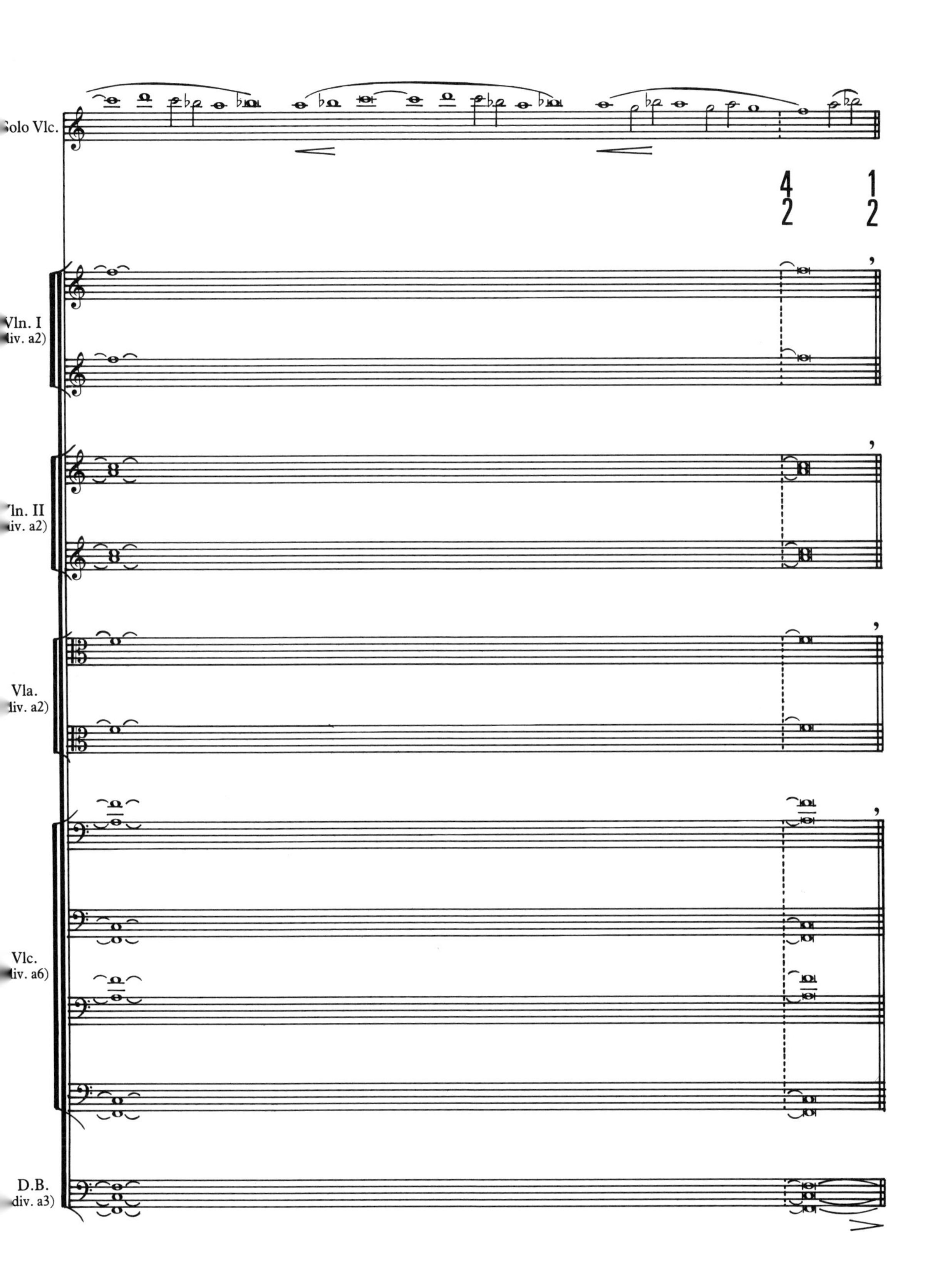
Solo Vlc.
4
2
1
2
Vln. I
(div. a2)
Vln. II
(div. a2)
Vla.
(div. a2)
Vlc.
(div. a6)
D.B.
(div. a3)

D
Solo Vlc.
p
1
2
3
2
5
2
3
2
6
2
3
2
Vln. I
(div. a2)
pp
poco
pp
poco
Vln. II
(div. a2)
pp
poco
pp
poco
Vla.
(div. a2)
pp
poco
pp
poco
Vlc.
(div. a2)
pp
poco
pp
poco
D.B.
(div. a3)
pp poss.

E
Transcendent, with awesome majesty
poco
mp
Solo Vlc.
3
2
5
2
3
2
poco
Vln. I
(div. a2)
Vln. II
(div. a2)
Vla.
(div. a2)
Vlc.
(div. a2)
D.B.
(div. a3)

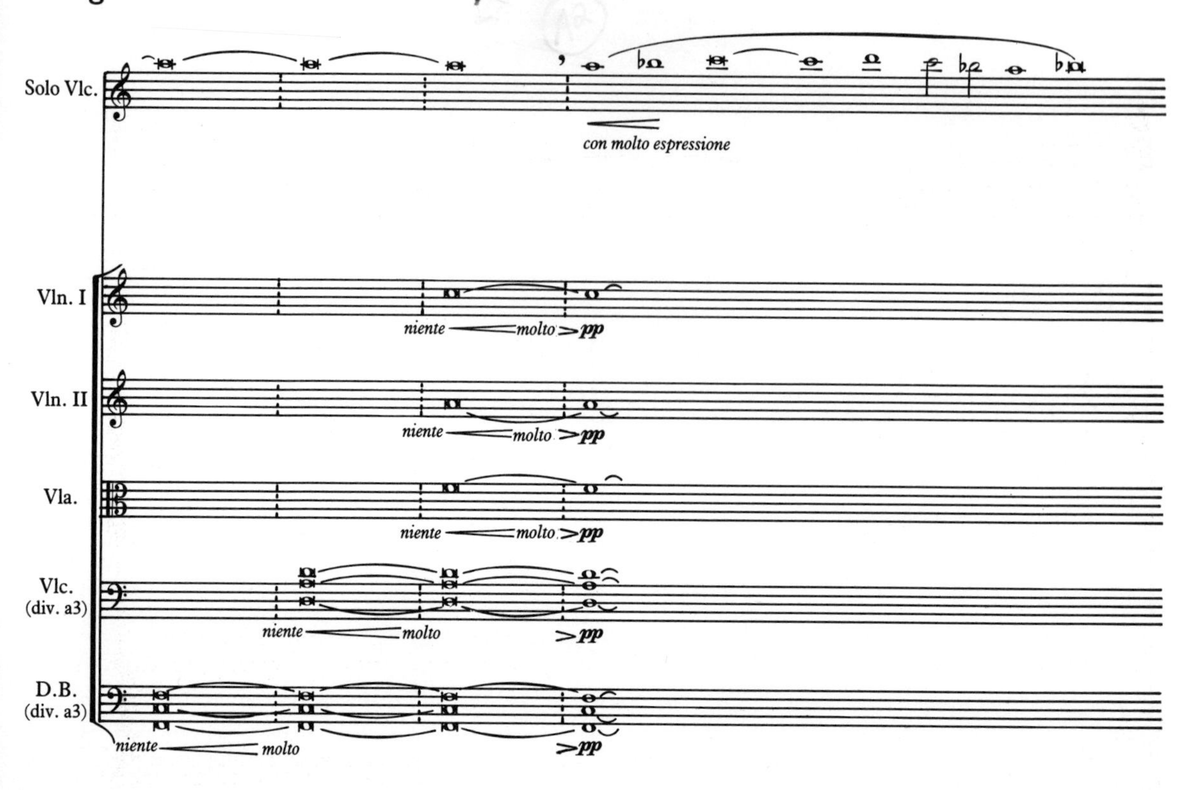
Solo Vlc.
con molto espressione
Vln. I
niente
molto
pp
Vln. II
niente
molto
pp
Vla.
niente
molto
pp
Vlc.
(div. a3)
niente
molto
pp
D.B.
(div. a3)
niente
molto
pp

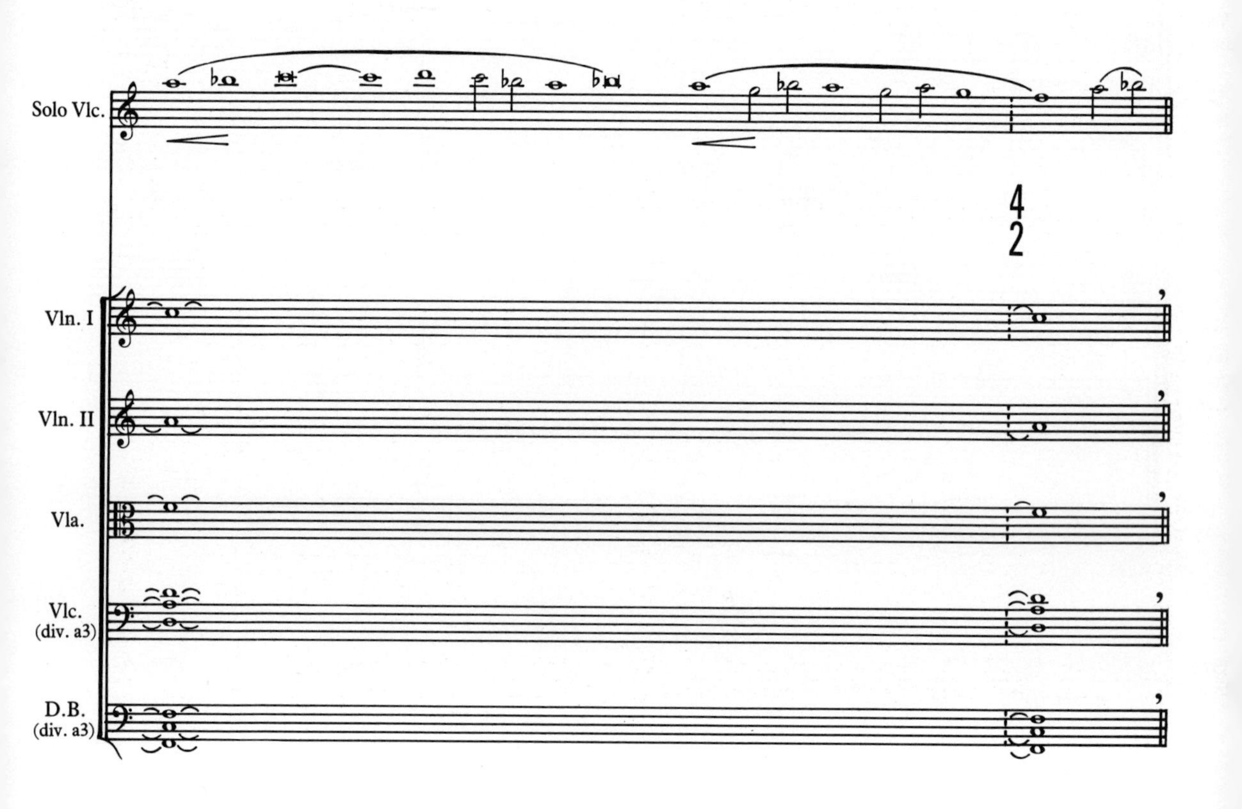
Solo Vlc.
4
2
Vln. I
Vln. II
Vla.
Vlc.
(div. a3)
D.B.
(div. a3)

F
Radiant
Solo Vlc.
sopra
8
2
6
2
4
2
Vln. I
(div. a2)
p
Vln. II
(div. a2)
Vla.
(div. a2)
Vlc.
(div. a6)
D.B.
(div. a3)

Solo Vlc.
3
2
6
2
3
2
4
2
Vln. I
(div. a2)
f
f
Vln. II
(div. a2)
f
f
Vla.
(div. a2)
f
f
Vlc.
(div. a6)
f
f
f
f
D.B.
(div. a3)

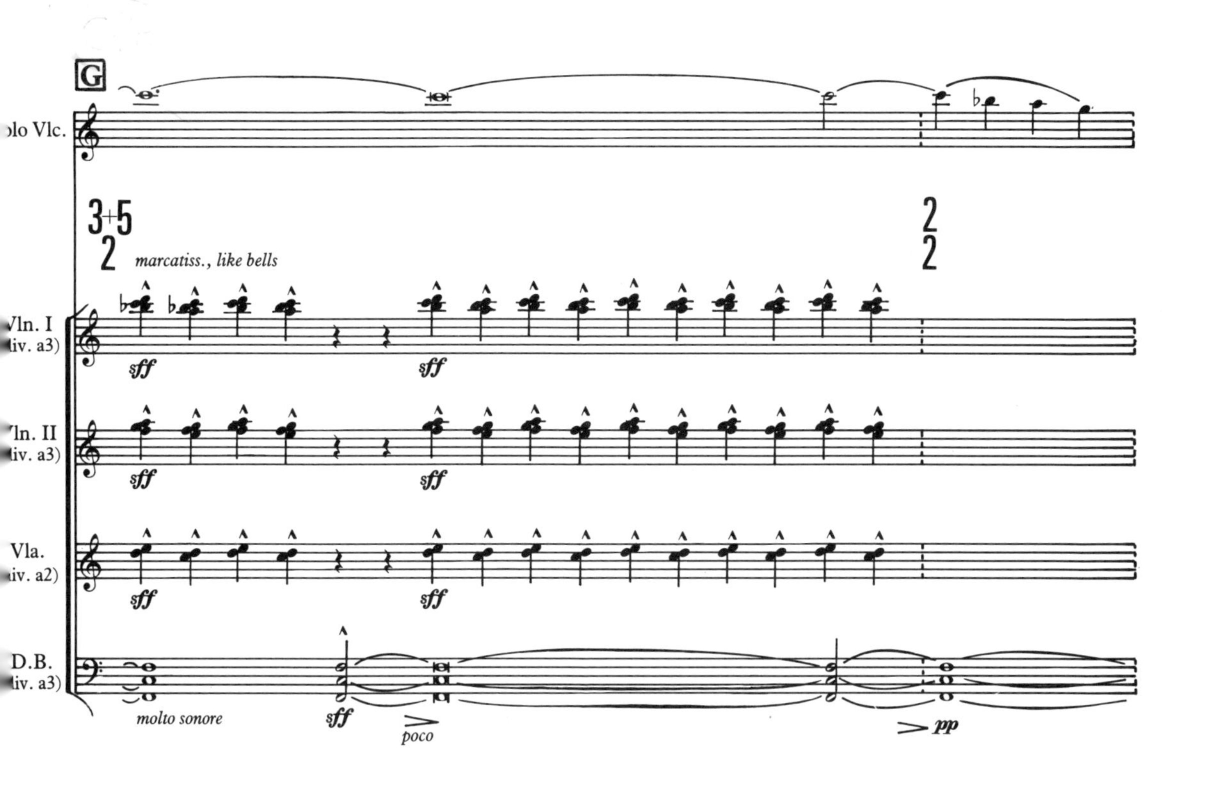

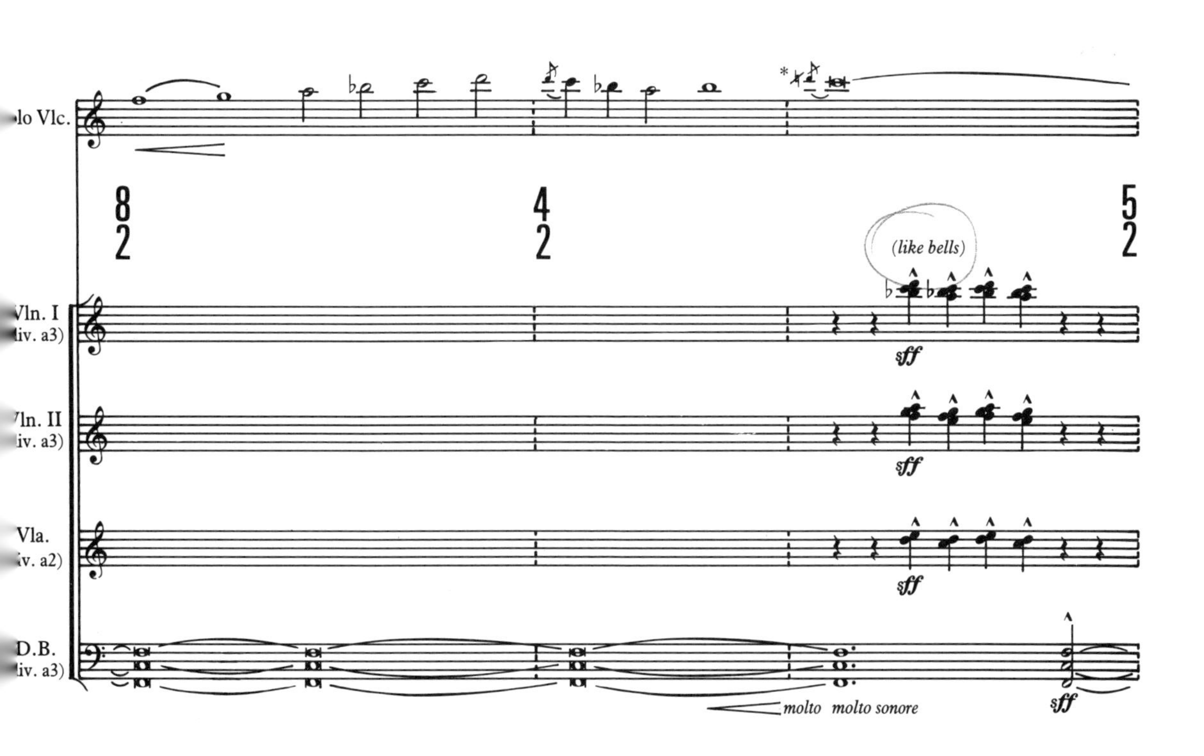

* ♮, ♯ and ♭ denote microtones, the characteristic 'breaks in the voice' of Byzantine chant.

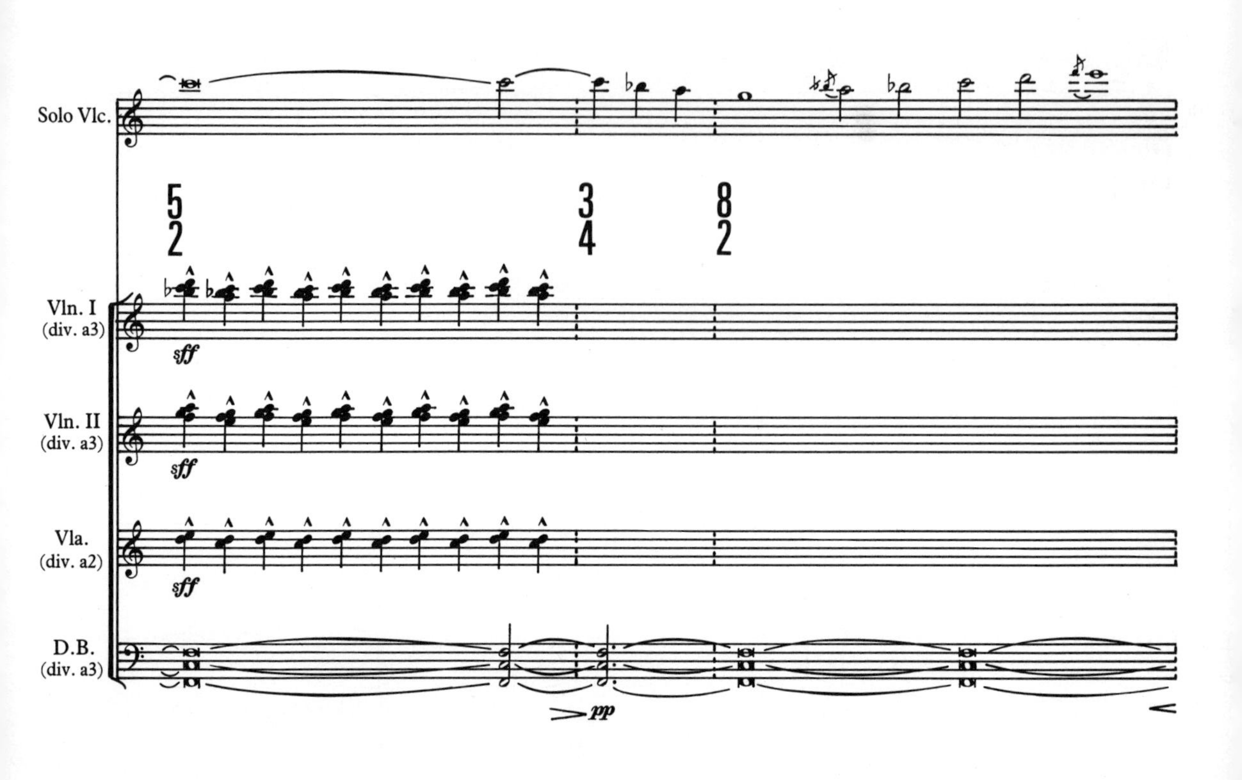
Solo Vlc.
Vln. I
(div. a3)
sff
Vln. II
(div. a3)
sff
Vla.
(div. a2)
sff
D.B.
(div. a3)
pp

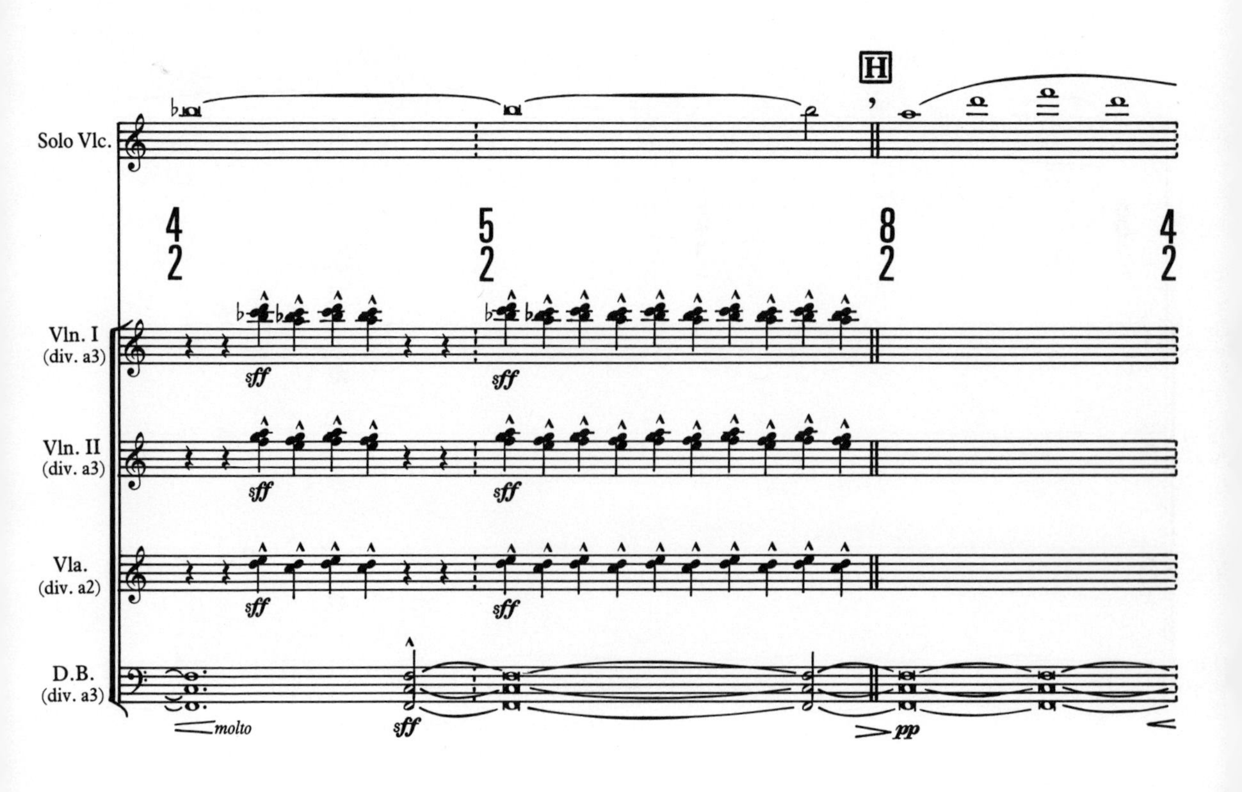
H
Solo Vlc.
Vln. I
(div. a3)
sff
sff
Vln. II
(div. a3)
sff
sff
Vla.
(div. a2)
sff
sff
D.B.
(div. a3)
molto
sff
pp

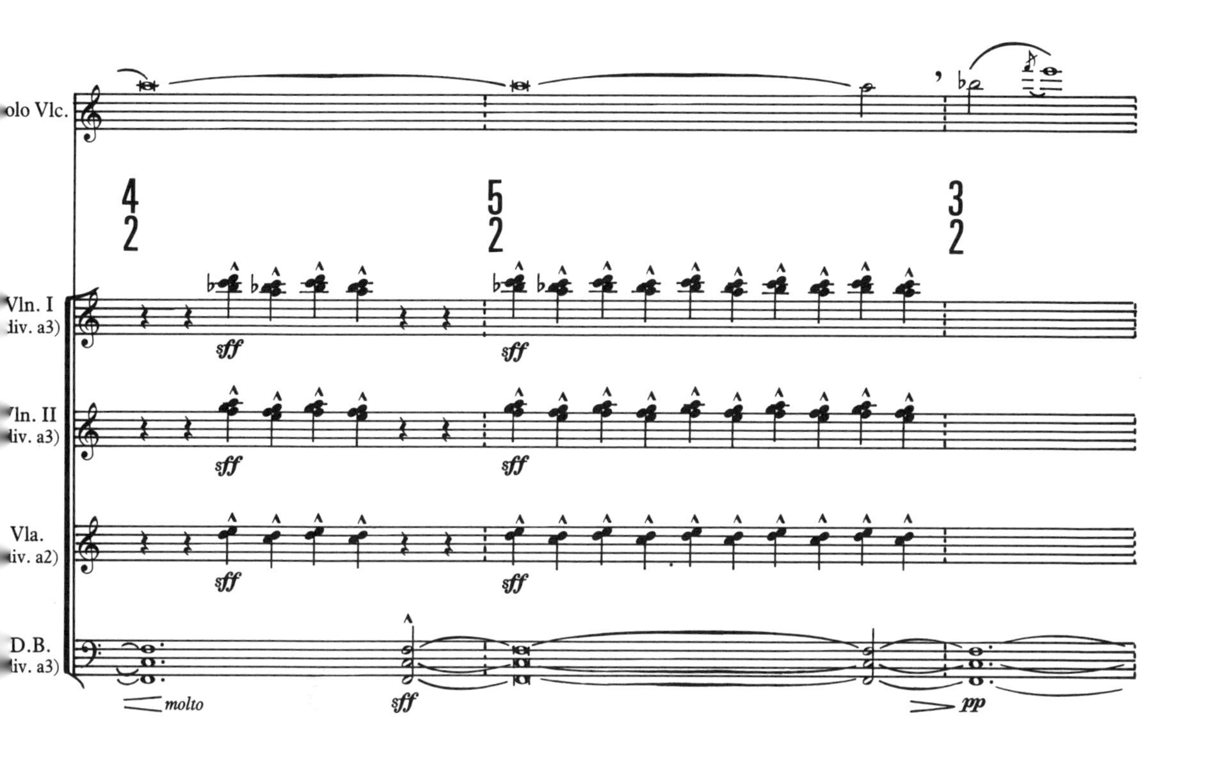
olo Vlc.
Vln. I
iv. a3)
Vln. II
iv. a3)
Vla.
iv. a2)
D.B.
iv. a3)
sff
molto
pp

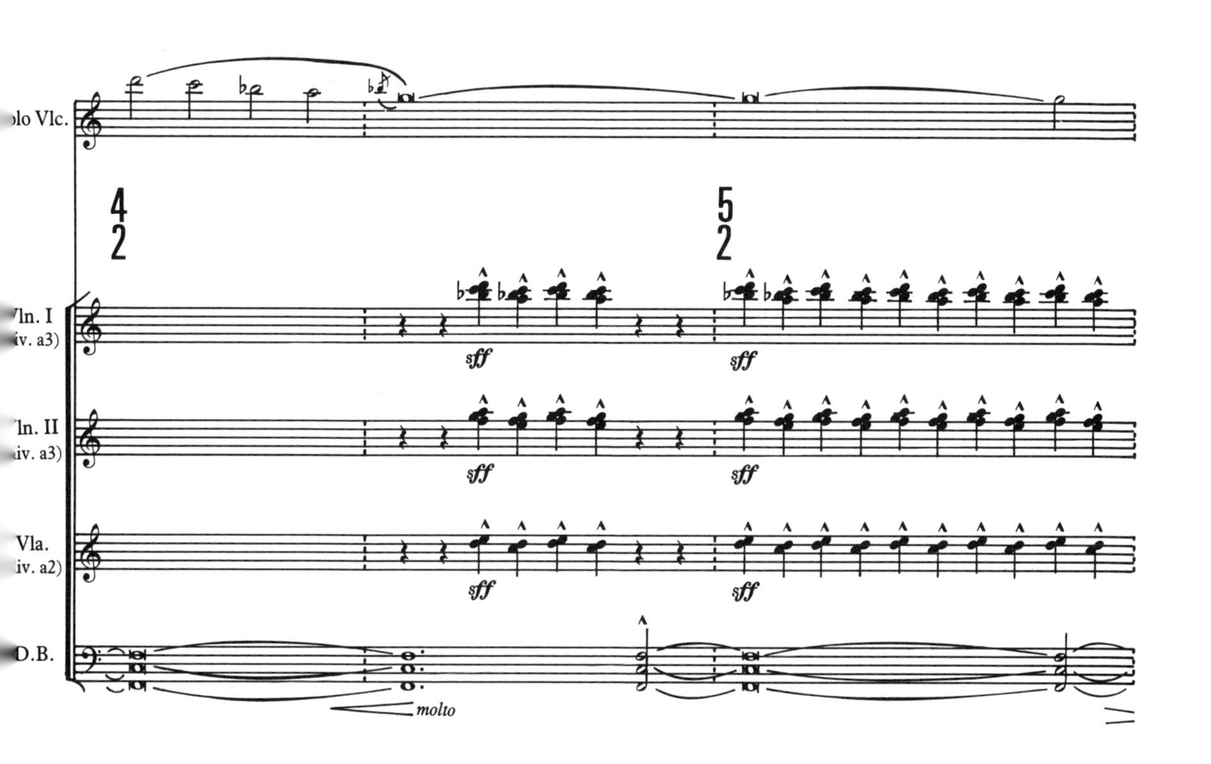
olo Vlc.
Vln. I
iv. a3)
Vln. II
iv. a3)
Vla.
iv. a2)
D.B.
sff
molto

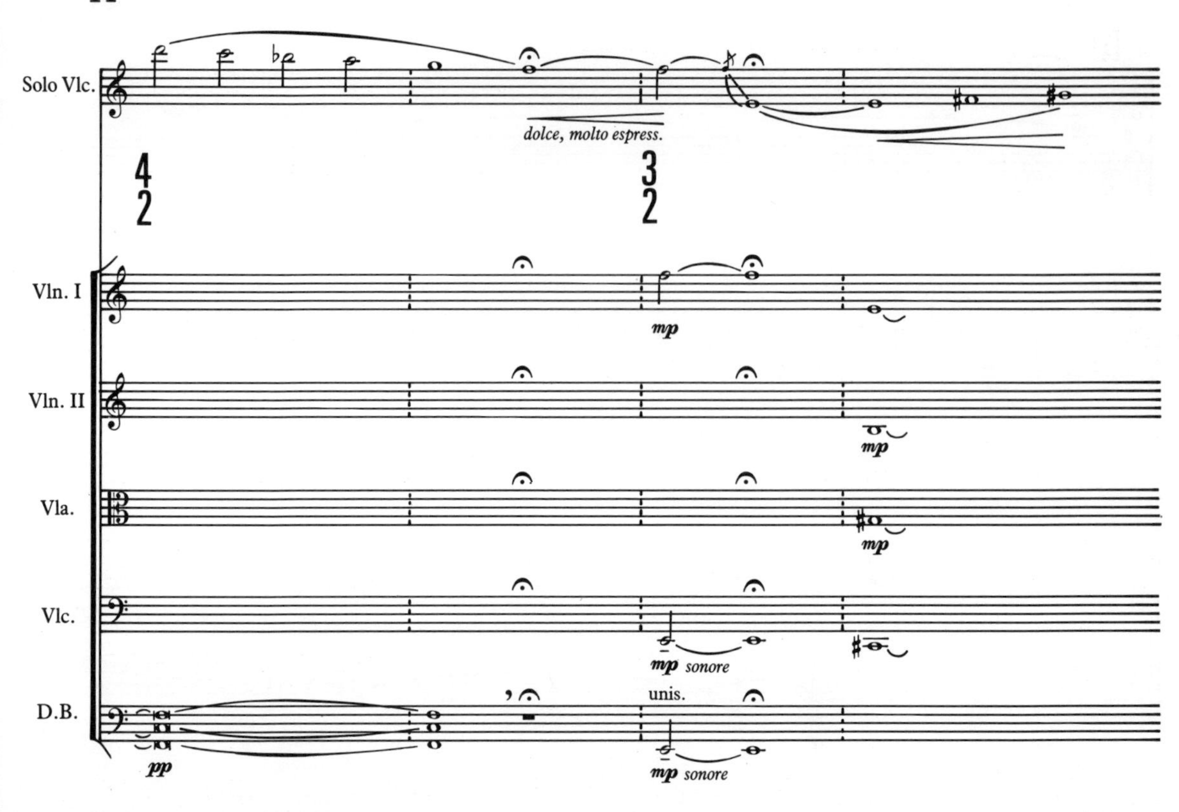
Solo Vlc.
dolce, molto espress.
Vln. I
mp
Vln. II
mp
Vla.
mp
Vlc.
mp sonore
D.B.
pp
unis.
mp sonore

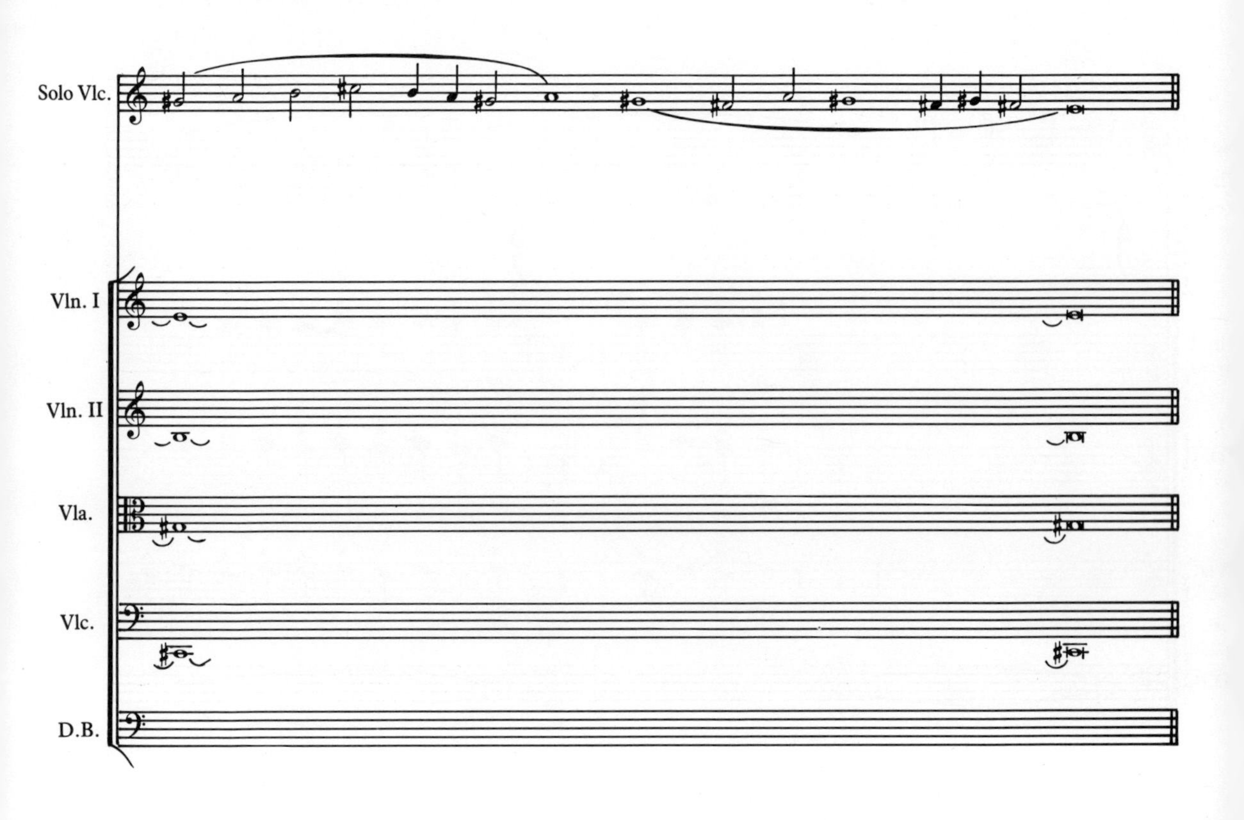
Solo Vlc.
Vln. I
Vln. II
Vla.
Vlc.
D.B.

I
olo Vlc.
gliss.
espress. e dolce
con sord.
pp poss.
loco
gliss.
ln. I
v. a4)
n. II
v. a4)
1. pp poss.
2. pp poss.
3. pp poss.
4.
Vla.
v. a4)
Vlc.
v. a2)
.B.
v. a2)

Solo Vlc.
Vln. I
(div. a4)
pp poss.
pp poss.
pp poss.
Vln. II
(div. a4)
pp poss.
pp poss.
pp poss.
Vla.
(div. a4)
gliss.
con sord.
Vlc.
(div. a2)
pp poss.
gliss.
con sord.
pp poss.
gliss.
D.B.
(div. a2)
gliss.
gliss.
pp poss.

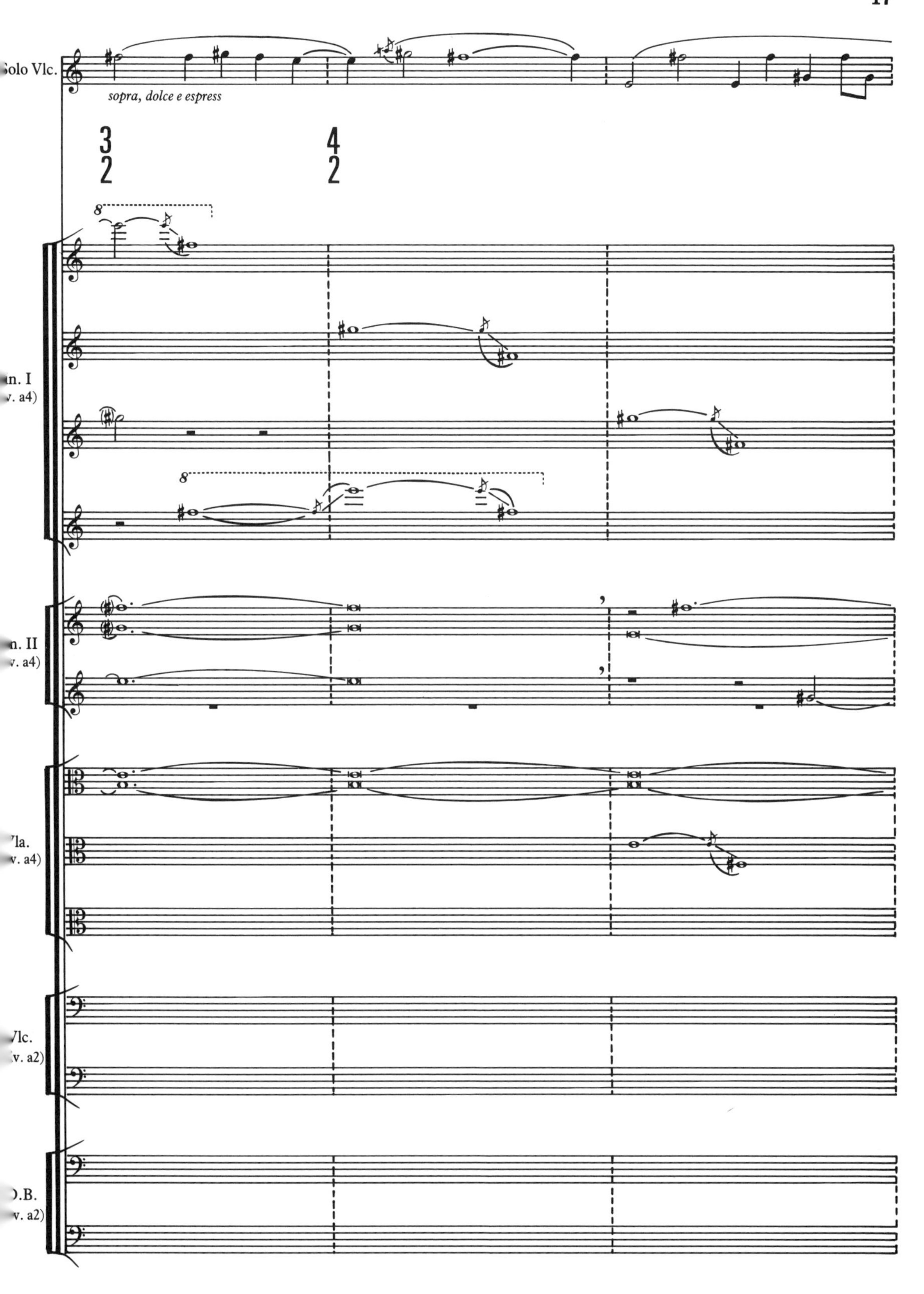
Solo Vlc.
sopra, dolce e espress
3
2
4
2
8
Vln. I
(div. a4)
8
Vln. II
(div. a4)
Vla.
(div. a4)
Vlc.
(div. a2)
D.B.
(div. a2)

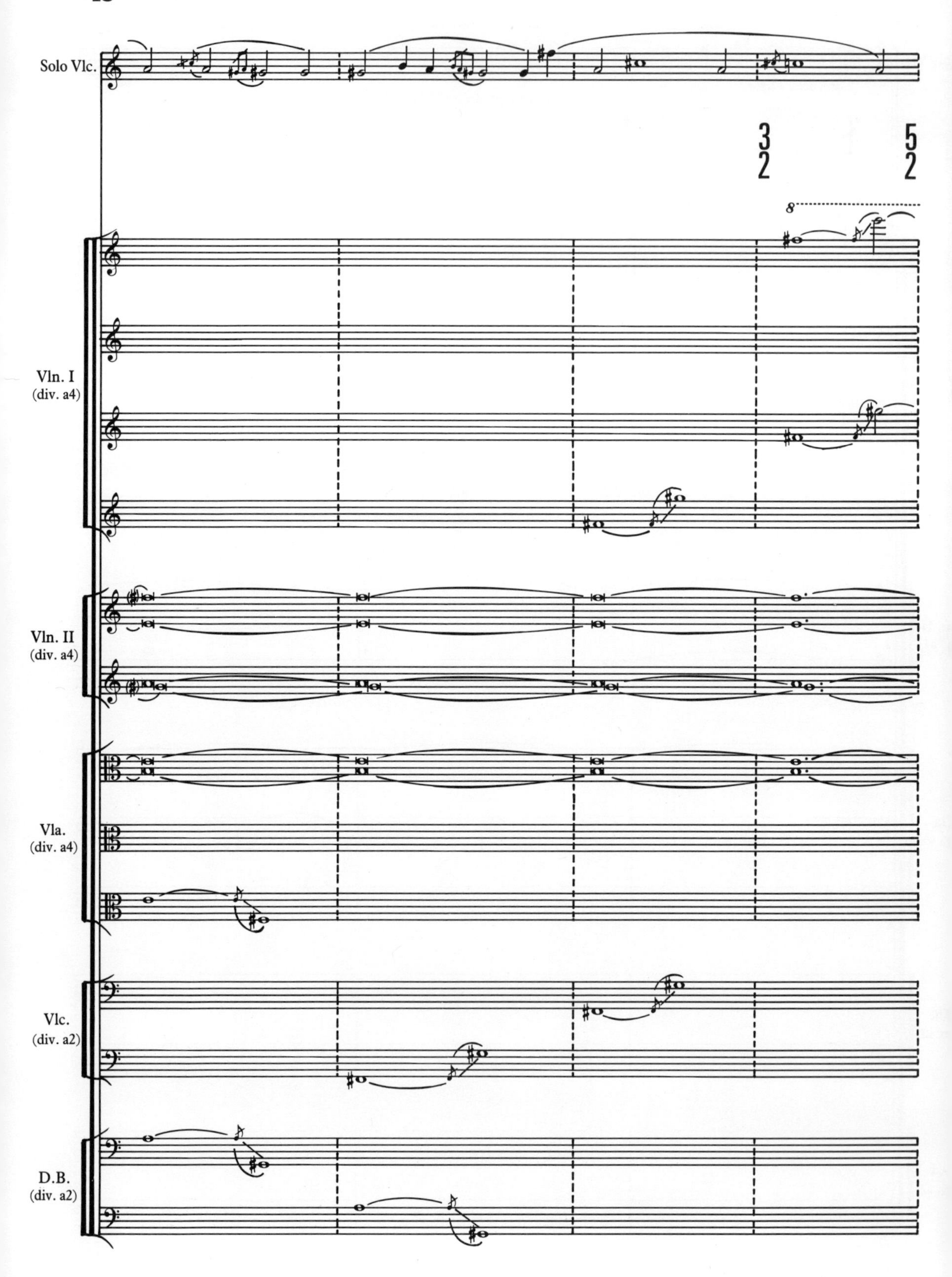
Solo Vlc.
3
2
5
2
8
Vln. I
(div. a4)
Vln. II
(div. a4)
Vla.
(div. a4)
Vlc.
(div. a2)
D.B.
(div. a2)

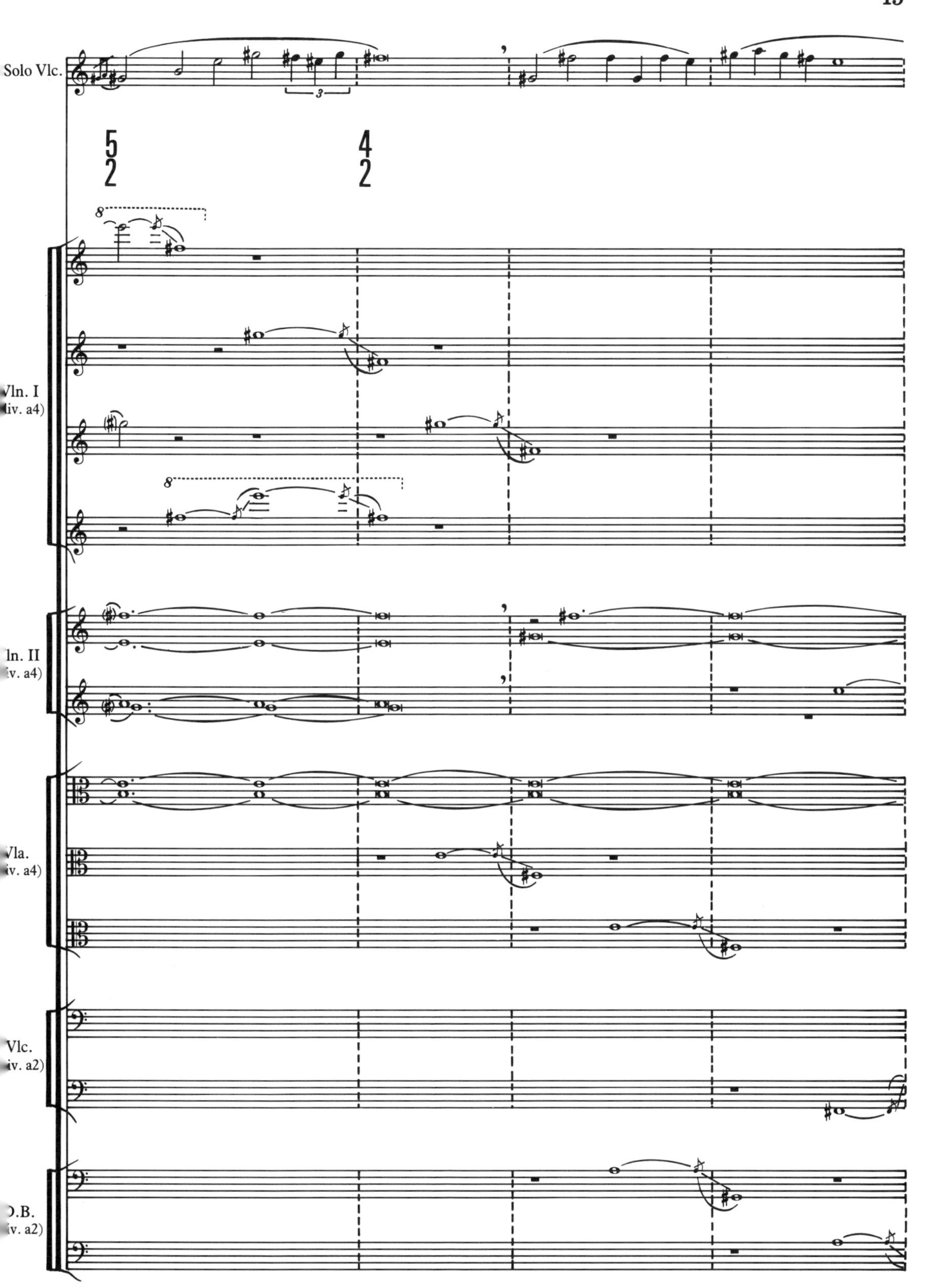
Solo Vlc.
Vln. I
Vla.
Vlc.

Solo Vlc.
8
8
Vln. I
(div. a4)
1.
2.
Vln. II
(div. a4)
Vla.
(div. a4)
Vlc.
(div. a2)
D.B.
(div. a2)

J
A little slower
lightly, without vibrato, like viols
olo Vlc.
mp leggiero
7
4
6
4
senza sord.
mp leggiero
Vlc.
(2 soli)
senza sord.
mp leggiero

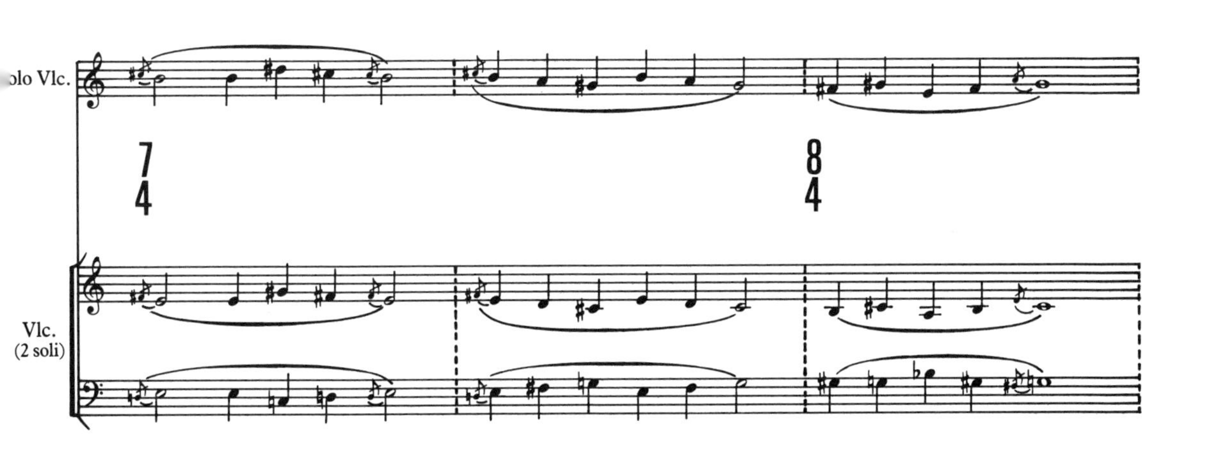
olo Vlc.
7
4
8
4
Vlc.
(2 soli)

olo Vlc.
7
4
5
4
4
2
Vlc.
(2 soli)
(segue)

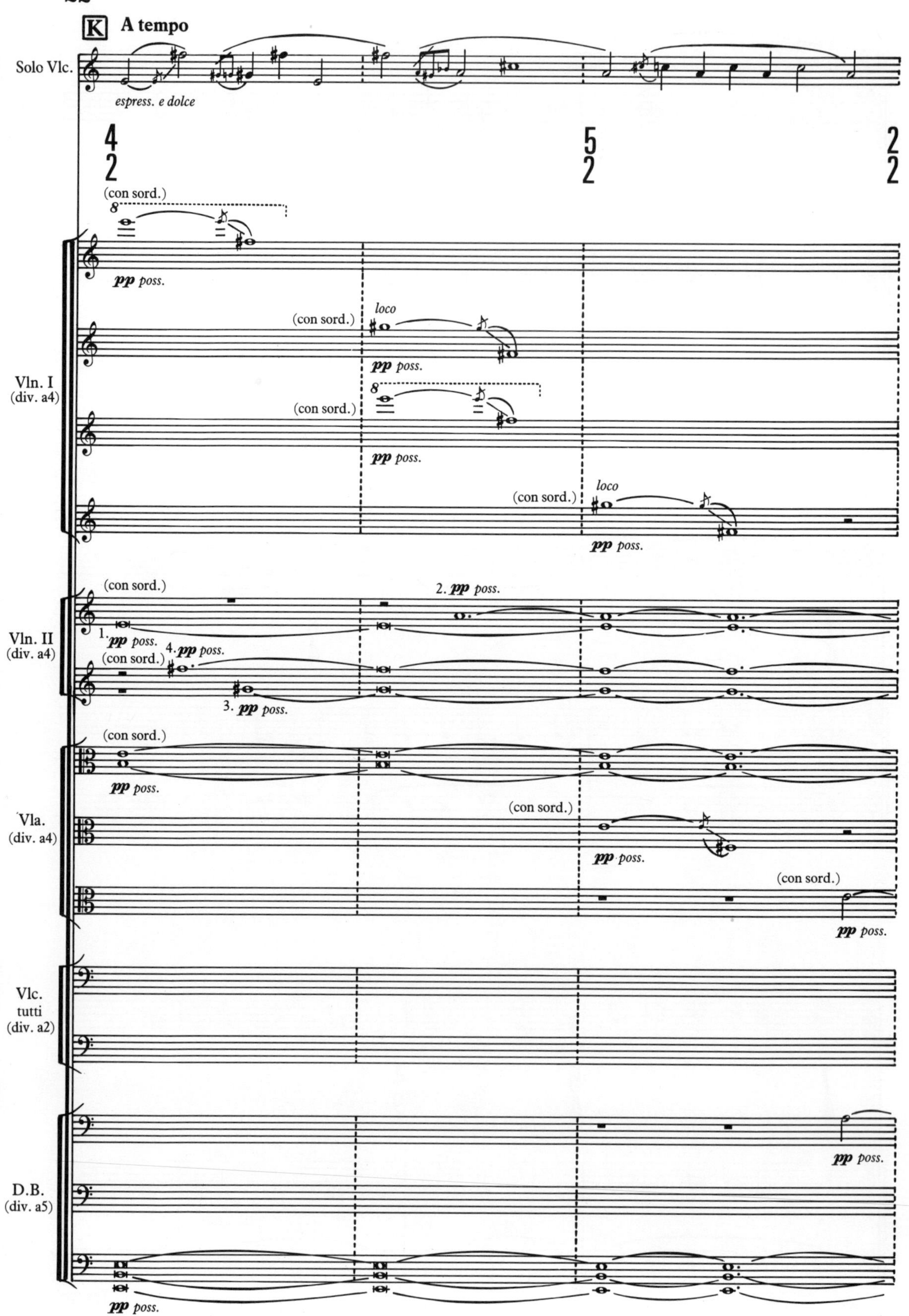
K
A tempo
Solo Vlc.
espress. e dolce
(con sord.)
8
pp poss.
(con sord.)
loco
pp poss.
Vln. I
(div. a4)
(con sord.)
8
pp poss.
(con sord.)
loco
pp poss.
(con sord.)
2. pp poss.
1. pp poss.
Vln. II
(div. a4)
4. pp poss.
(con sord.)
3. pp poss.
(con sord.)
pp poss.
Vla.
(div. a4)
(con sord.)
pp poss.
(con sord.)
pp poss.
Vlc.
tutti
(div. a2)
pp poss.
D.B.
(div. a5)
pp poss.

Solo Vlc.
2
2
4
2
Vln. I
(div. a4)
Vln. II
(div. a4)
Vla.
(div. a4)
Vlc.
(div. a2)
con sord.
pp poss.
D.B.
(div. a5)
(tutti, div. a3)
like bells
sff molto sonore
pp poss.
sff molto sonore
sff molto sonore

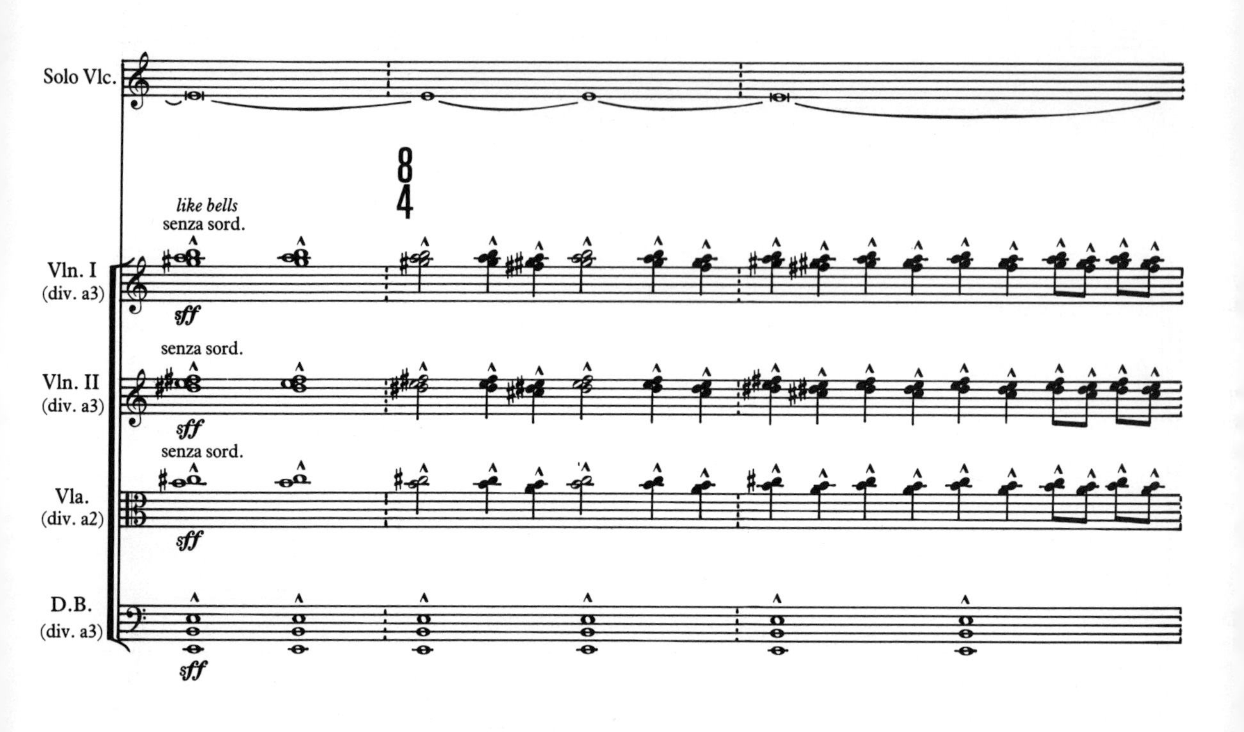
Solo Vlc.
like bells
senza sord.
Vln. I
(div. a3)
sff
senza sord.
Vln. II
(div. a3)
sff
senza sord.
Vla.
(div. a2)
sff
D.B.
(div. a3)
sff

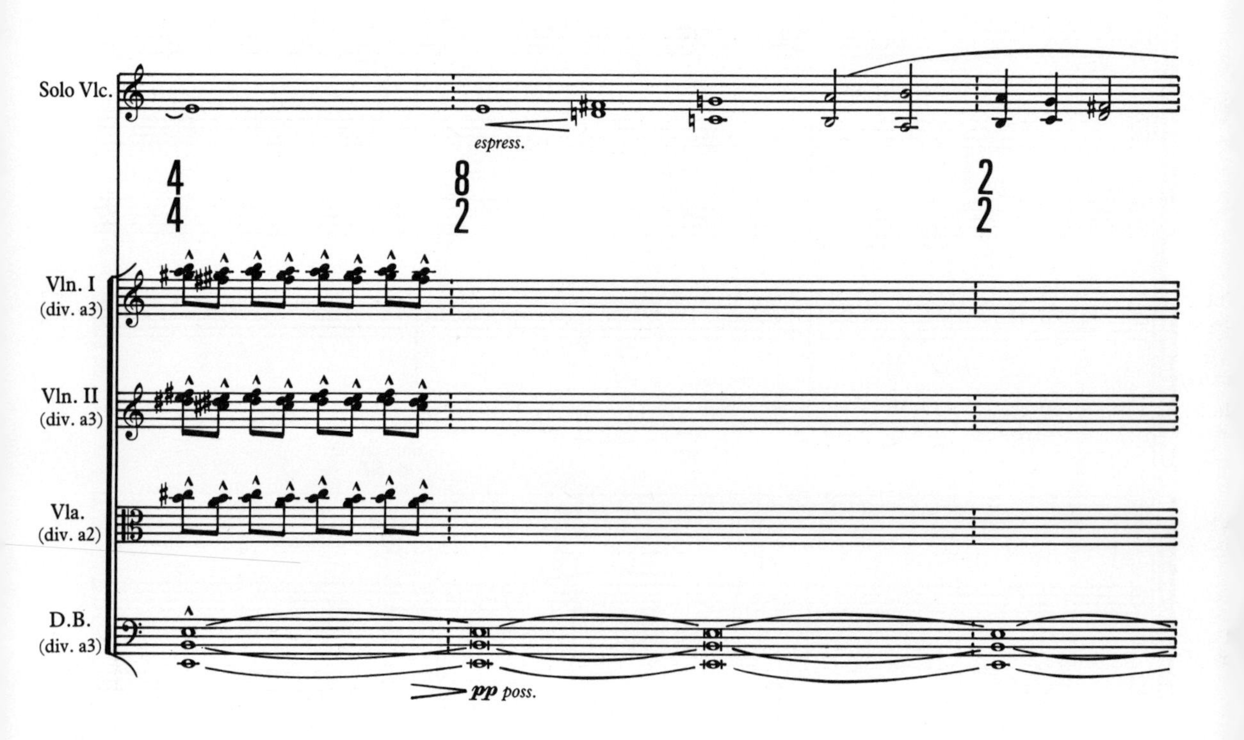
Solo Vlc.
espress.
Vln. I
(div. a3)
Vln. II
(div. a3)
Vla.
(div. a2)
D.B.
(div. a3)
pp poss.

olo Vlc.
4
2
4
4
Vln. I
iiv. a3)
sff
Vln. II
iiv. a3)
sff
Vla.
iiv. a2)
sff
D.B.
iiv. a3)
molto
sff

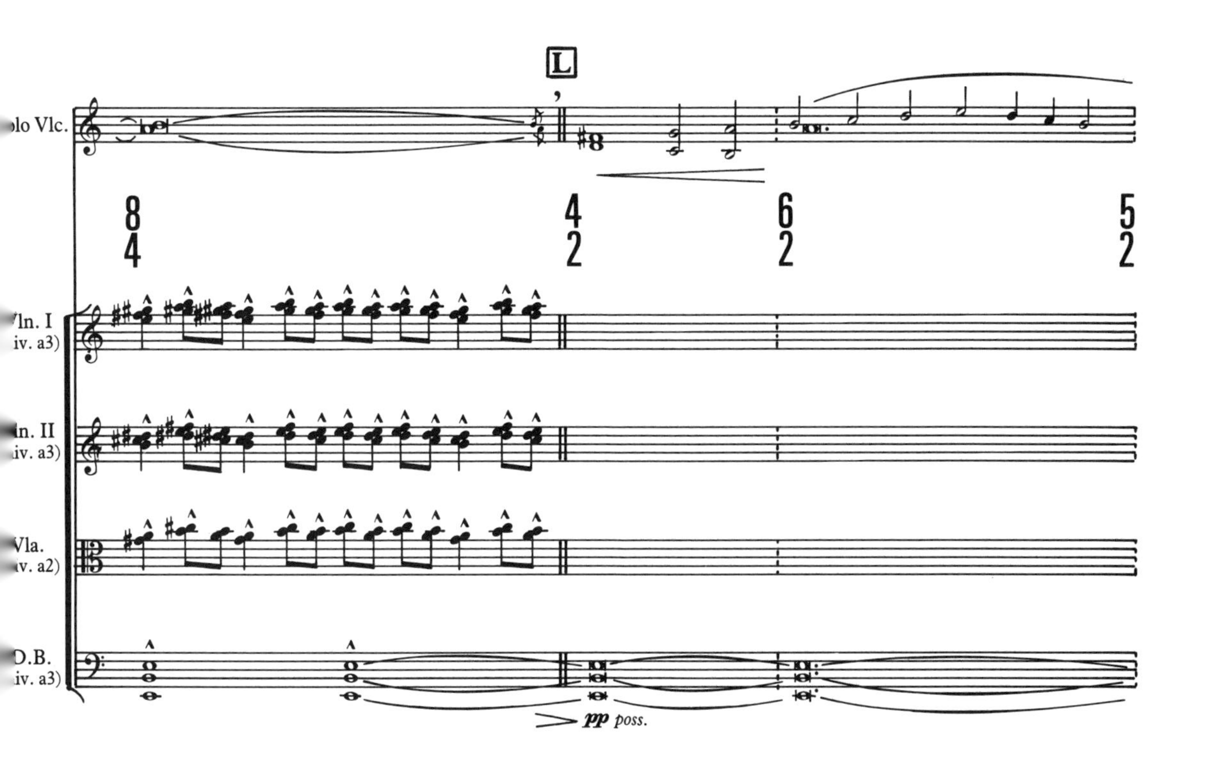
L
olo Vlc.
8
4
4
2
6
2
5
2
Vln. I
iv. a3)
ln. II
iv. a3)
Vla.
iv. a2)
D.B.
iv. a3)
pp poss.

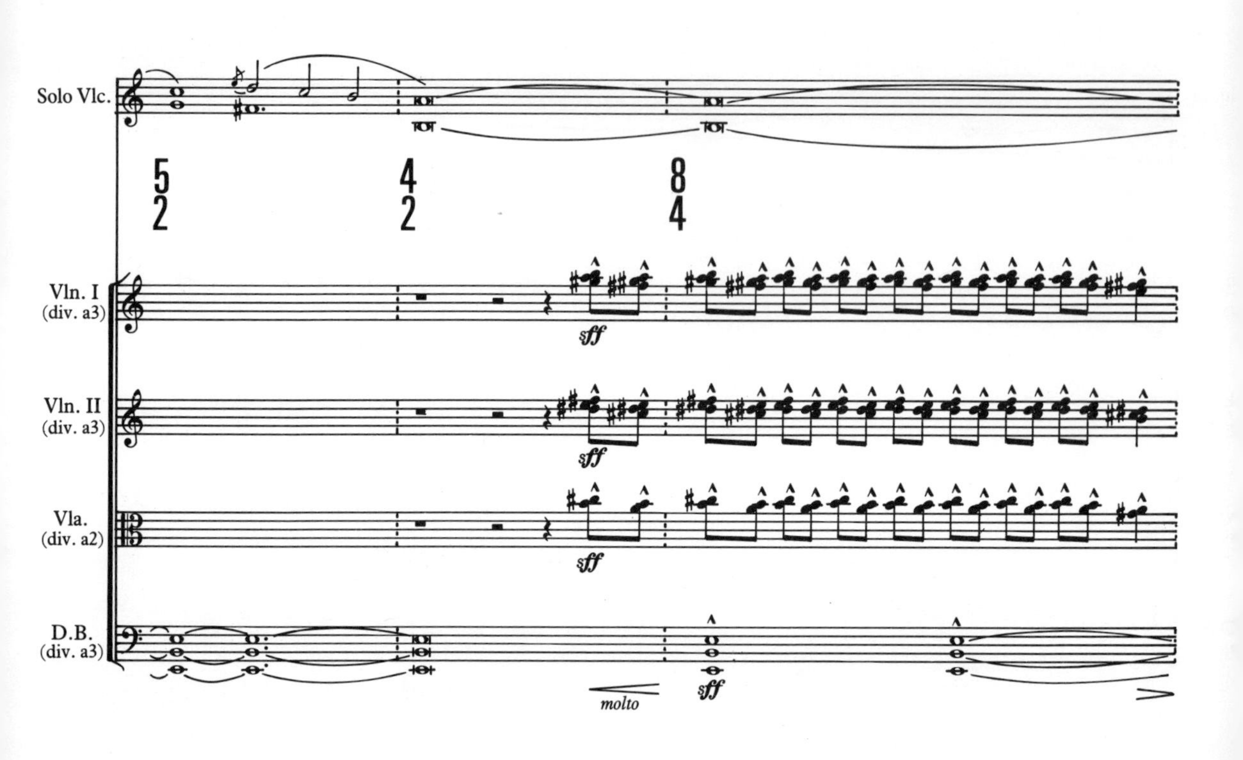
Solo Vlc.
Vln. I
(div. a3)
sff
Vln. II
(div. a3)
sff
Vla.
(div. a2)
sff
D.B.
(div. a3)
molto
sff

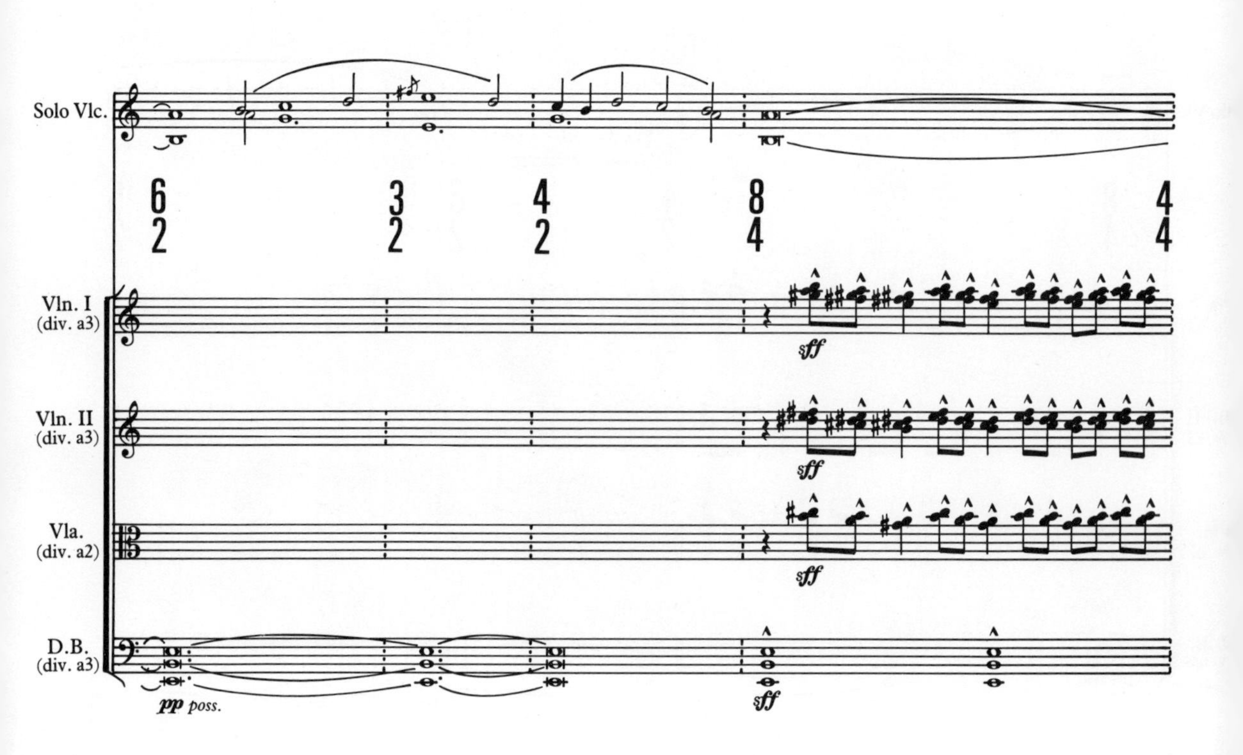
Solo Vlc.
Vln. I
(div. a3)
sff
Vln. II
(div. a3)
sff
Vla.
(div. a2)
sff
D.B.
(div. a3)
pp poss.
sff

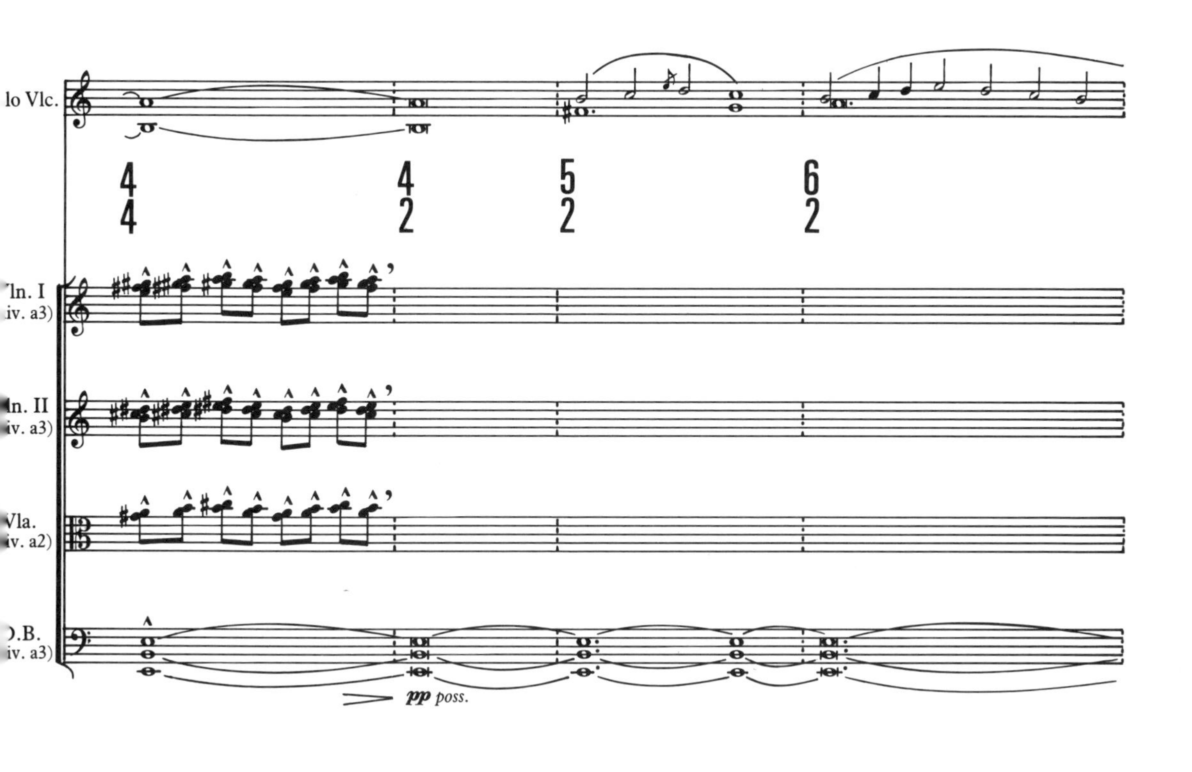
lo Vlc.
4
4
4
2
5
2
6
2
'ln. I
iv. a3)
ln. II
iv. a3)
Vla.
iv. a2)
).B.
iv. a3)
pp poss.

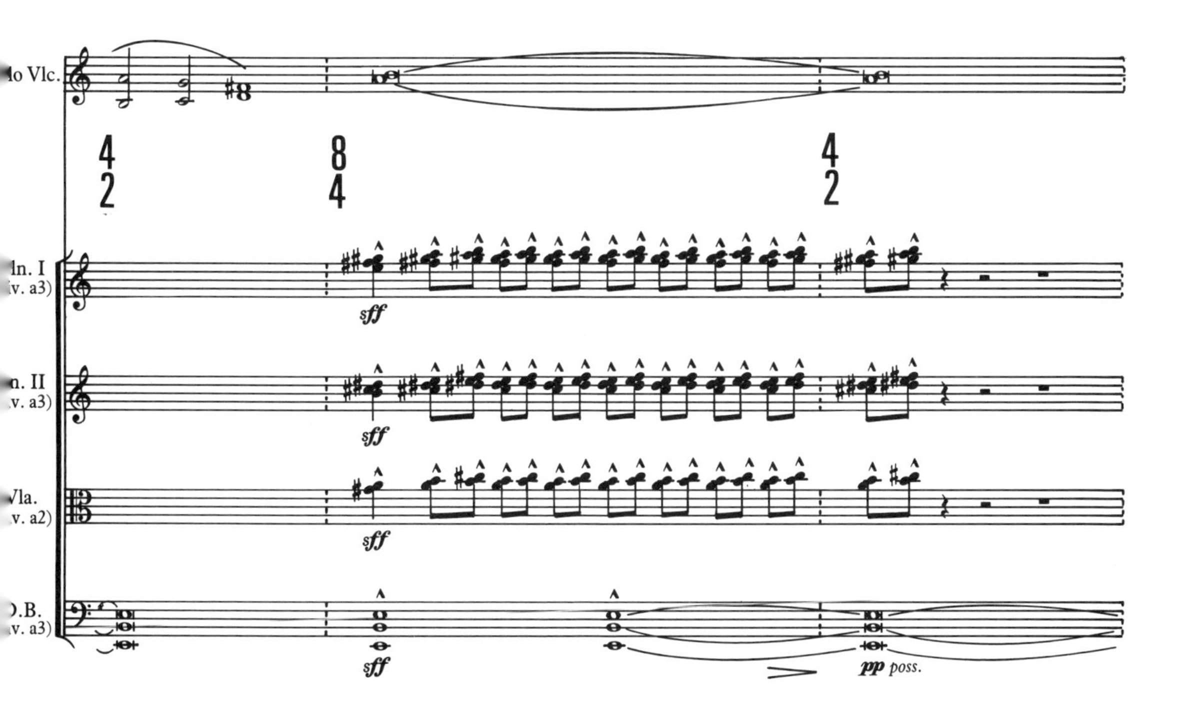
lo Vlc.
4
2
8
4
4
2
ln. I
iv. a3)
sff
n. II
v. a3)
sff
Vla.
v. a2)
sff
).B.
v. a3)
sff
pp poss.

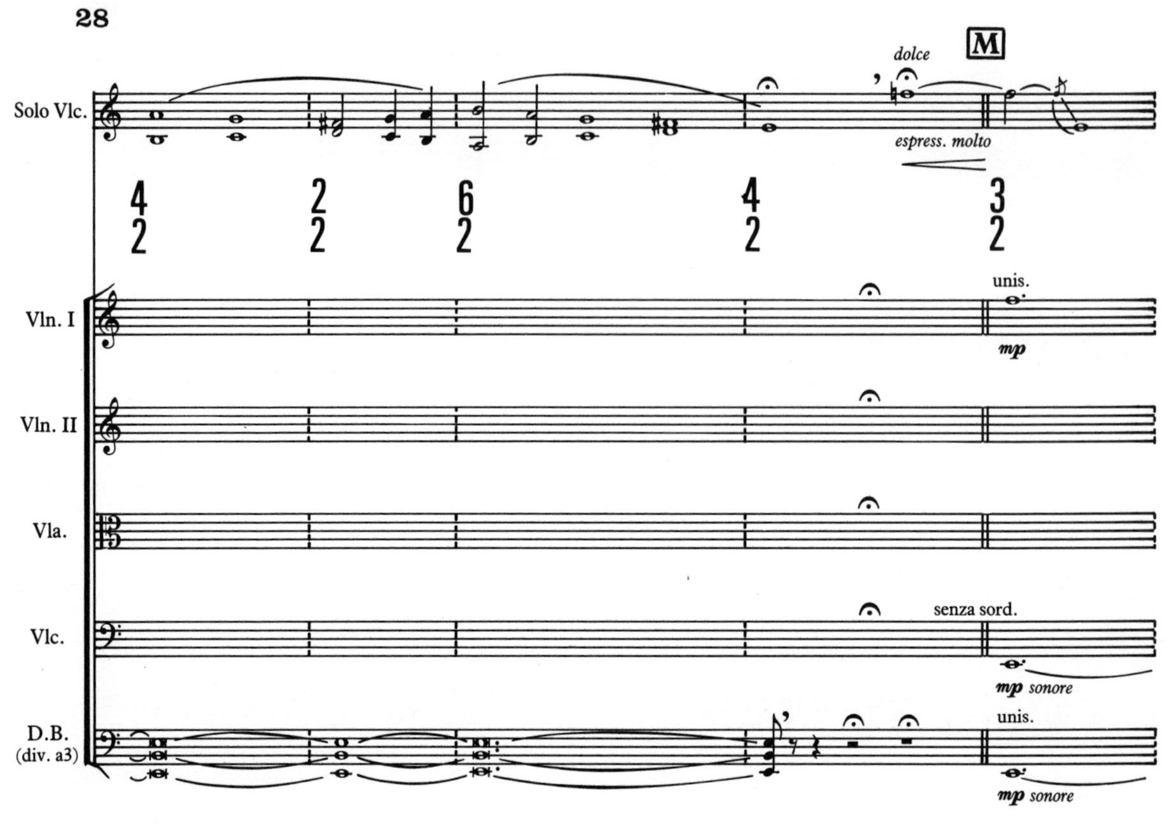
M
dolce
Solo Vlc.
espress. molto
Vln. I
unis.
mp
Vln. II
Vla.
Vlc.
senza sord.
mp sonore
D.B.
(div. a3)
unis.
mp sonore

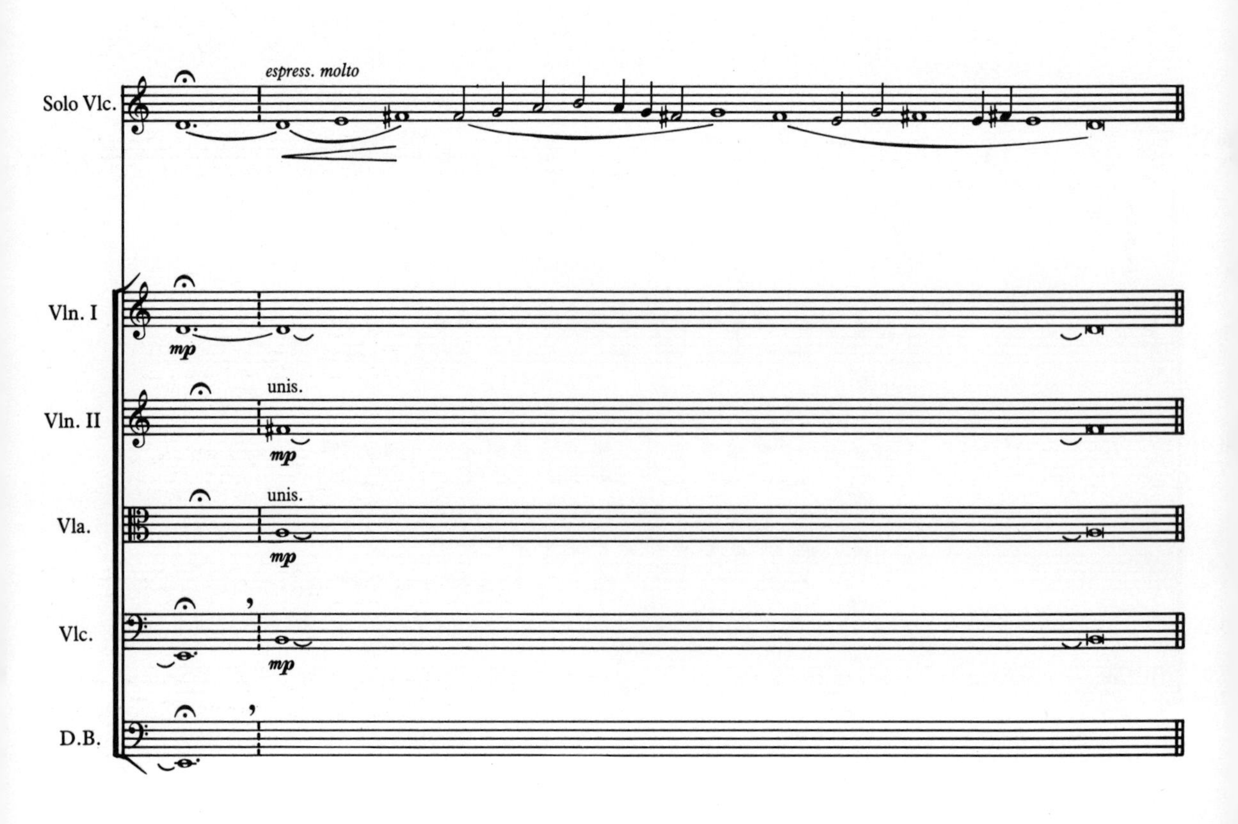
Solo Vlc.
espress. molto
Vln. I
mp
Vln. II
unis.
mp
Vla.
unis.
mp
Vlc.
mp
D.B.

N
ANNUNCIATION
Moving forward
o Vlc.
sopra
4
2
pp non legato
n. I
v. a2)
pp non legato
n. II
iv. a2)
poco fp
poco
sim.
Vla.
poco fp
poco
sim.
lc.
. a4)
poco fp
poco
sim.
).B.
poco fp
poco
sim.

Solo Vlc.
Vln. I
(div. a2)
Vln. II
(div. a2)
Vla.
Vlc.
(div. a4)
D.B.
Solo Vlc.
Vln. I
(div. a2)
Vln. II
(div. a2)
Vla.
Vlc.
(div. a4)
D.B.

olo Vlc.
Vln. I
(div. a2)
Vln. II
(div. a2)
Vla.
Vlc.
(div. a4)
D.B.
olo Vlc.
Vln. I
(div. a2)
Vln. II
(div. a2)
Vla.
Vlc.
(div. a4)
D.B.

Solo Vlc.
Vln. I
(div. a2)
Vln. II
(div. a2)
Vla.
Vlc.
(div. a4)
D.B.
O

olo Vlc.
8
Vln. I
iv. a2)
Vln. II
div. a2)
Vla.
Vlc.
v. a4)
D.B.

Solo Vlc.
Vln. I
(div. a2)
Vln. II
(div. a2)
Vla.
Vlc.
(div. a4)
D.B.
Solo Vlc.
Vln. I
(div. a2)
Vln. II
(div. a2)
Vla.
Vlc.
(div. a4)
D.B.

olo Vlc.
Vln. I
iv. a2)
Vln. II
div. a2)
Vla.
Vlc.
v. a4)
D.B.
poco rit.
52

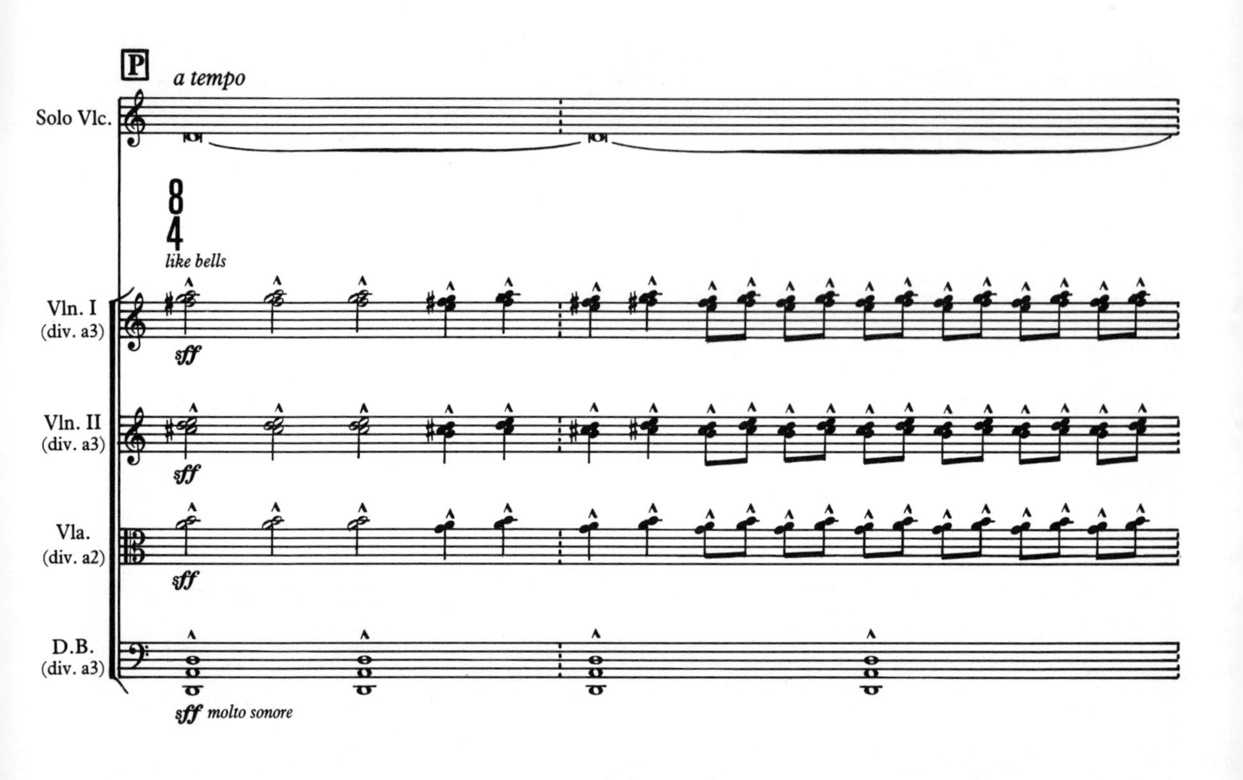
P
a tempo
Solo Vlc.
8
4
like bells
Vln. I
(div. a3)
sff
Vln. II
(div. a3)
sff
Vla.
(div. a2)
sff
D.B.
(div. a3)
sff molto sonore

Solo Vlc.
5
2
Vln. I
(div. a3)
Vln. II
(div. a3)
Vla.
(div. a2)
D.B.
(div. a3)
pp poss.

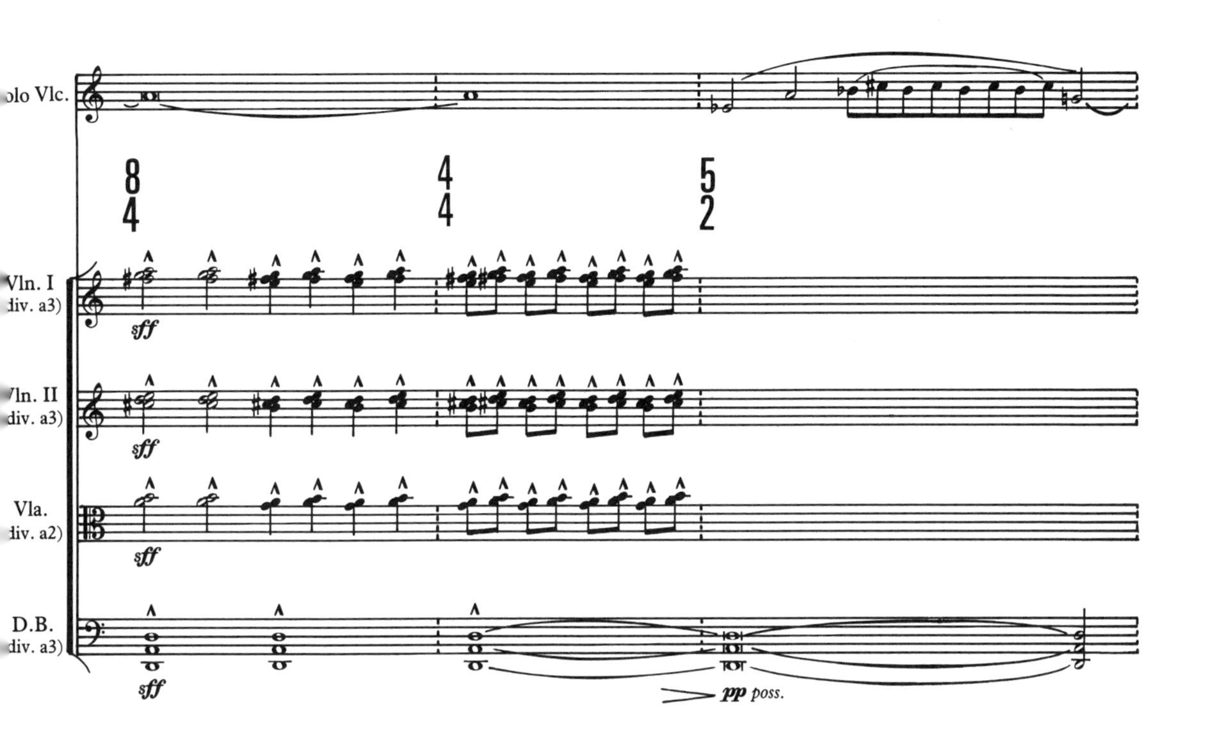
olo Vlc.
Vln. I
div. a3)
sff
Vln. II
div. a3)
sff
Vla.
div. a2)
sff
D.B.
div. a3)
sff
pp poss.

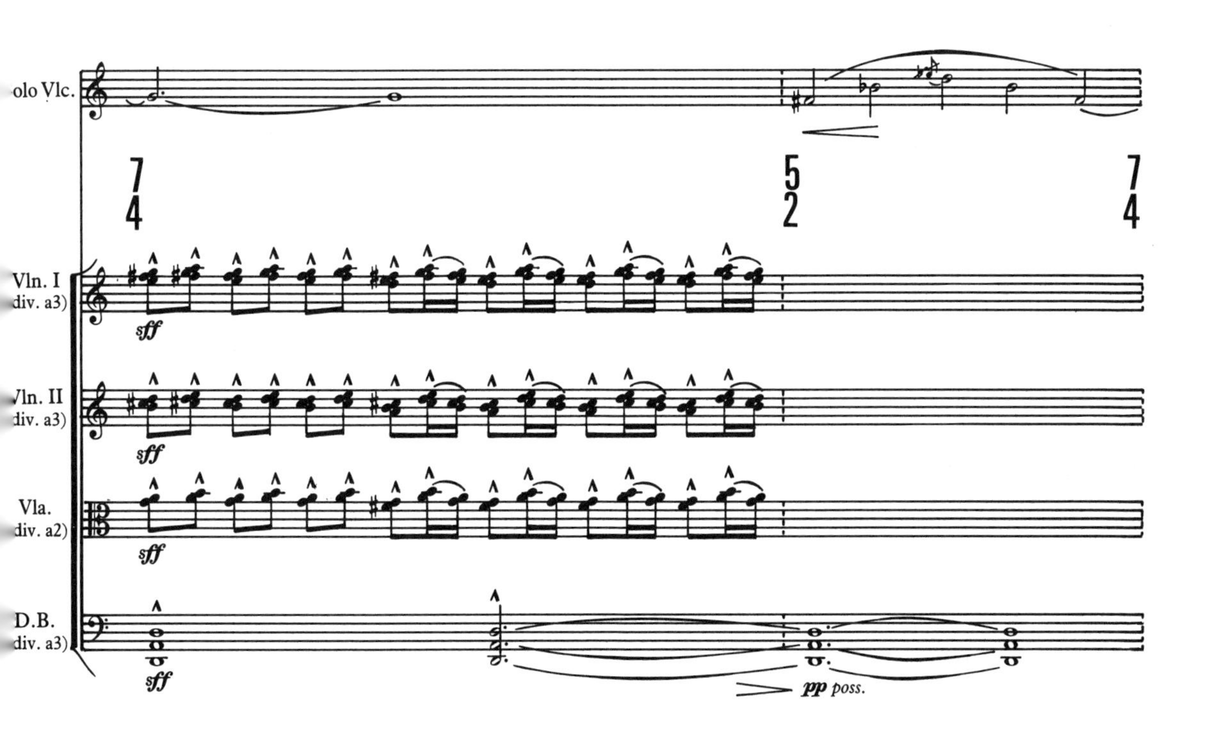
olo Vlc.
Vln. I
div. a3)
sff
Vln. II
div. a3)
sff
Vla.
div. a2)
sff
D.B.
div. a3)
sff
pp poss.

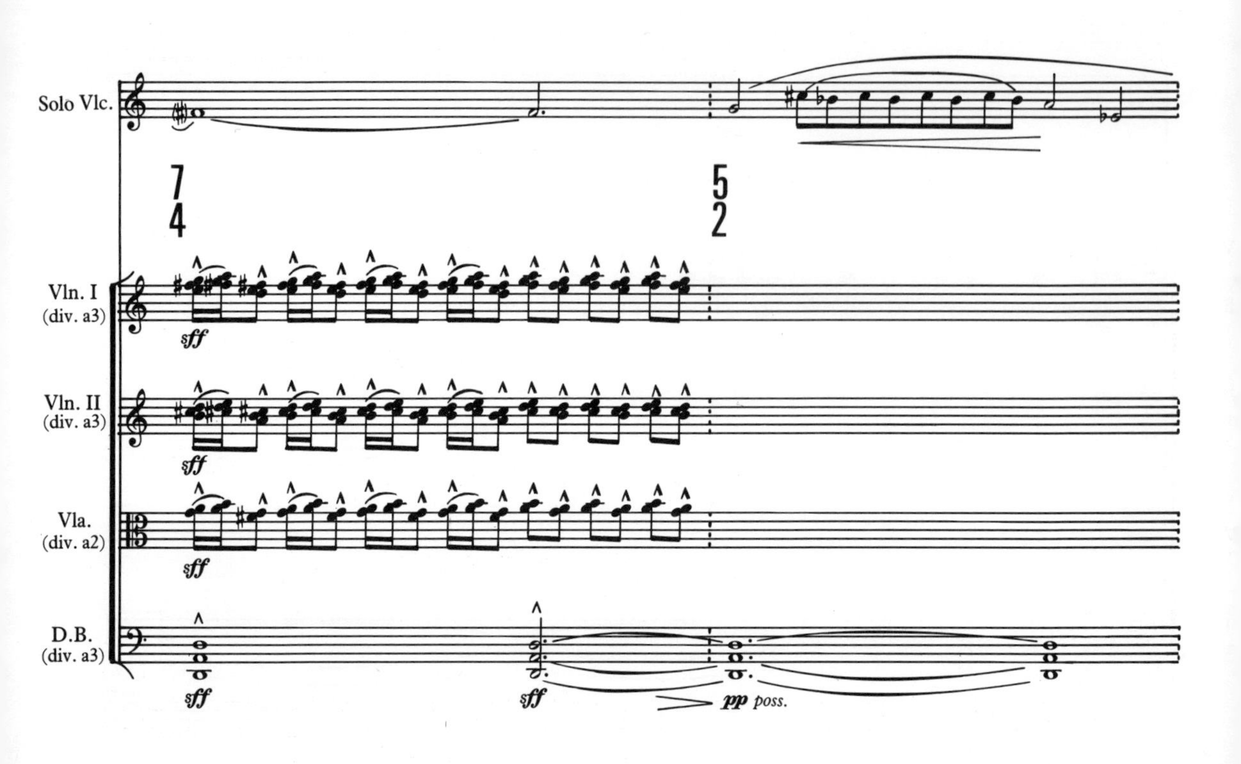
Solo Vlc.
7
4
5
2
Vln. I
(div. a3)
sff
Vln. II
(div. a3)
sff
Vla.
(div. a2)
sff
D.B.
(div. a3)
sff
sff
pp poss.

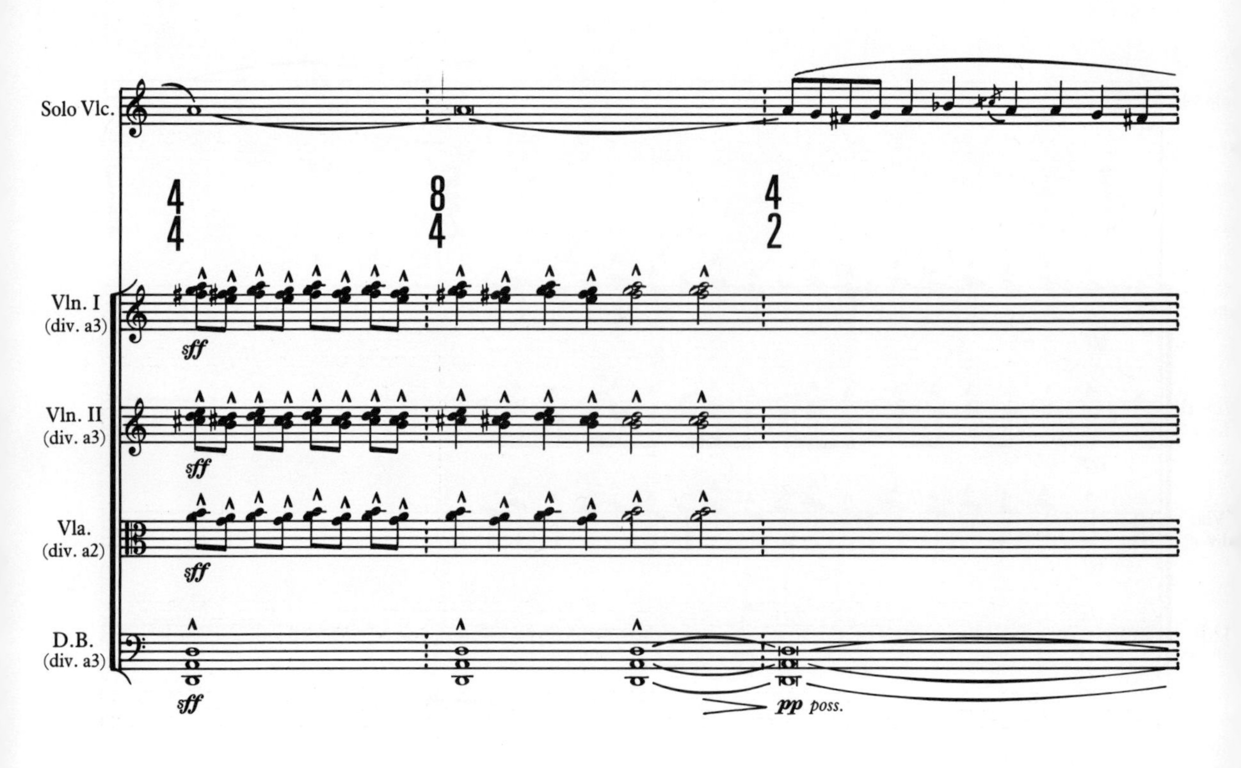
Solo Vlc.
4
4
8
4
4
2
Vln. I
(div. a3)
sff
Vln. II
(div. a3)
sff
Vla.
(div. a2)
sff
D.B.
(div. a3)
sff
pp poss.

Q
dolce
espress. molto
Solo Vlc.
Vln. I
mp
Vlc.
(div. a5)
mp sonore
D.B.
espress. molto
mp

Modulated to C   Byzantine connections

THE INCARNATION

Moving forward – always very freely

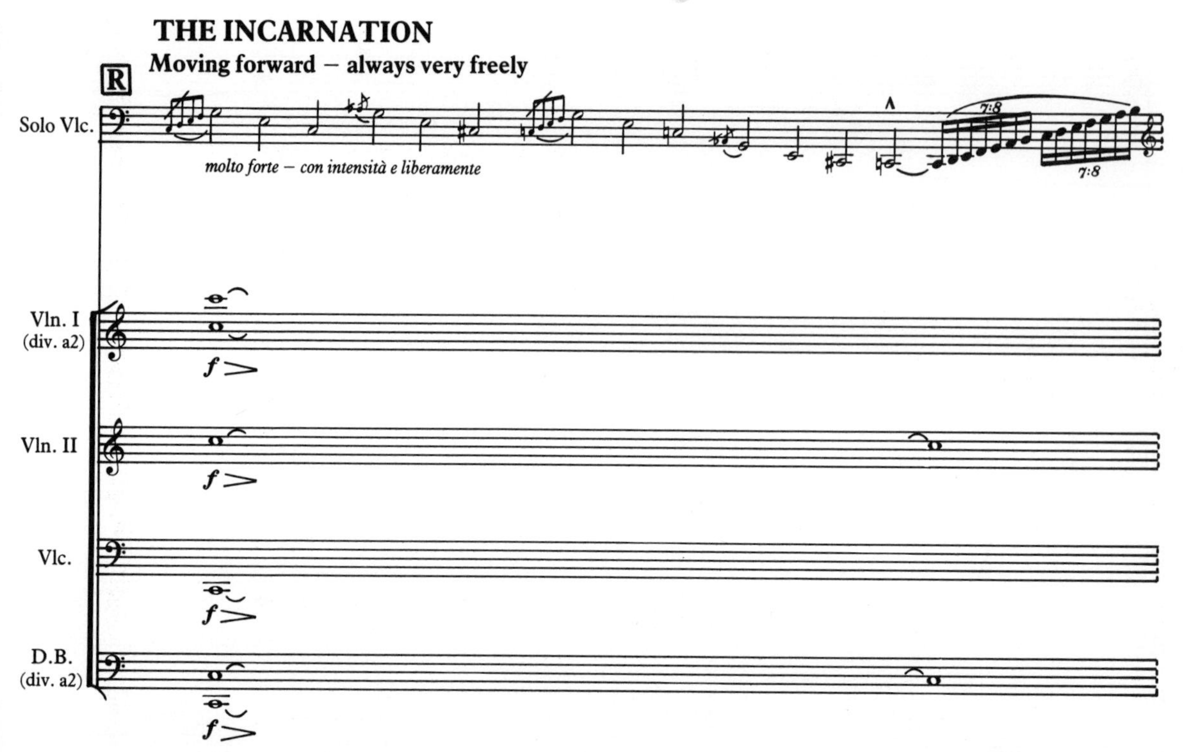

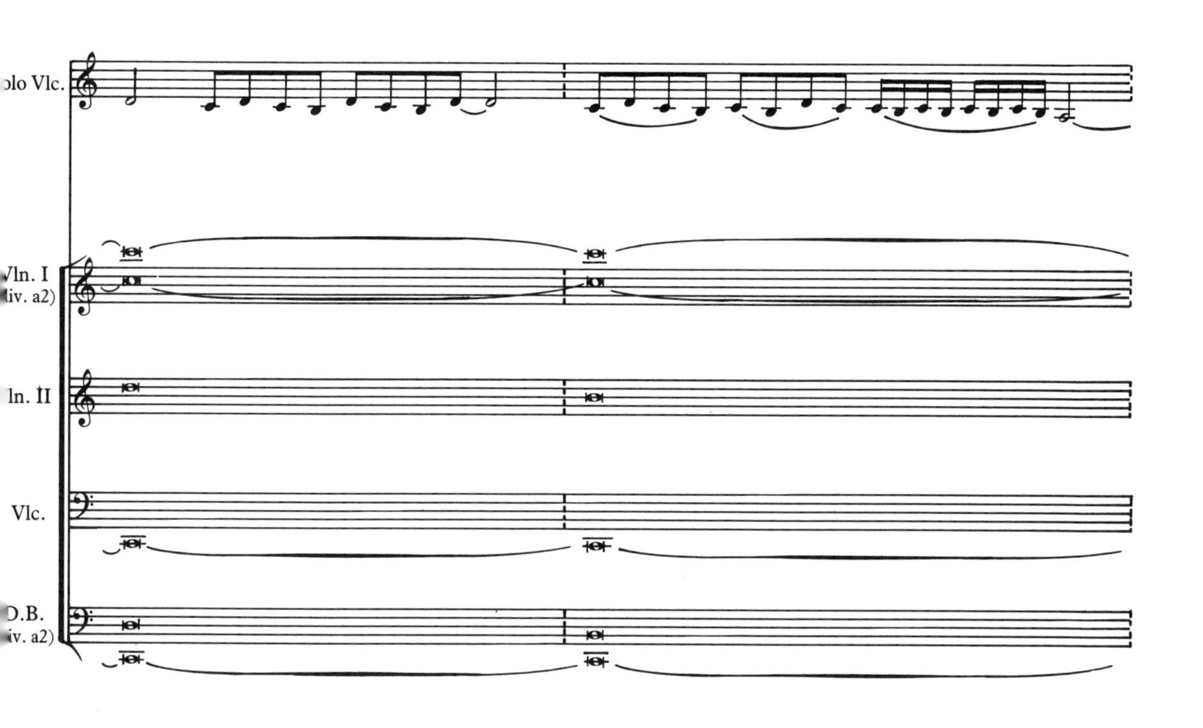
olo Vlc.
Vln. I
iv. a2)
ln. II
Vlc.
D.B.
iv. a2)

olo Vlc.
Vln. I
iv. a2)
ln. II
Vlc.
D.B.
iv. a2)

Solo Vlc.
Vln. I
(div. a2)
Vln. II
Vlc.
D.B.
(div. a2)

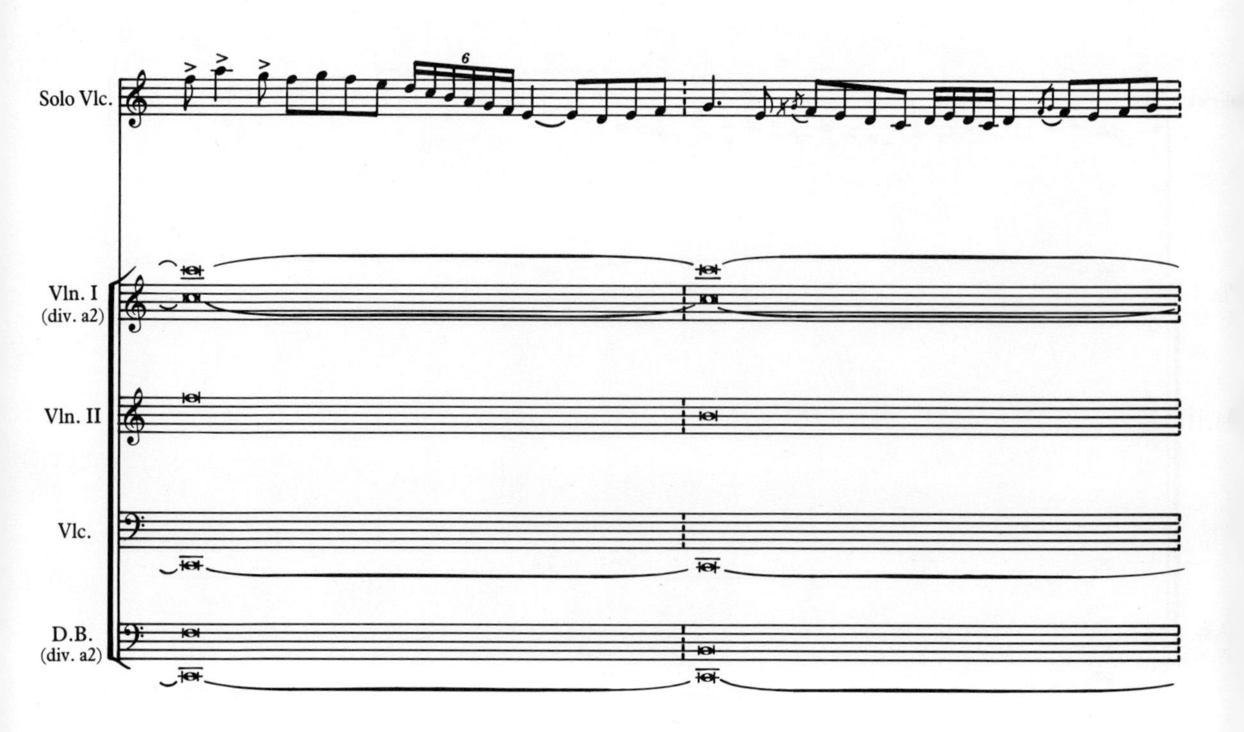
Solo Vlc.
Vln. I
(div. a2)
Vln. II
Vlc.
D.B.
(div. a2)

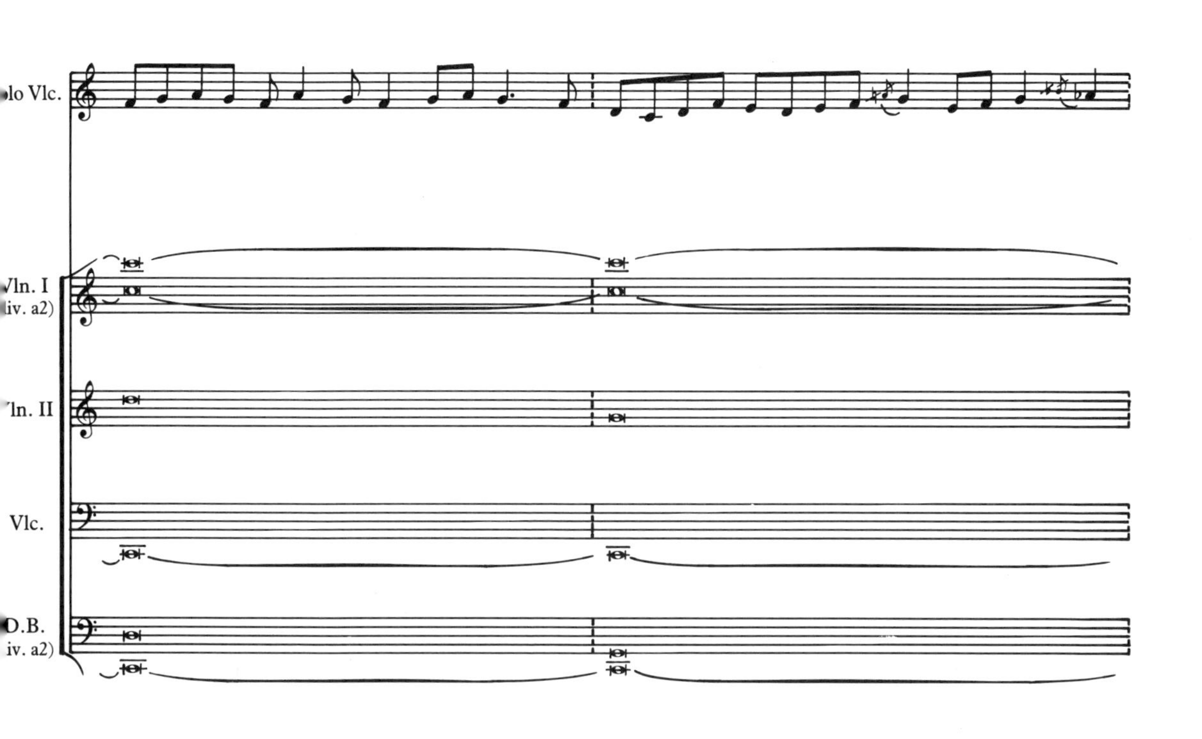
lo Vlc.
Vln. I
iv. a2)
'ln. II
Vlc.
D.B.
iv. a2)

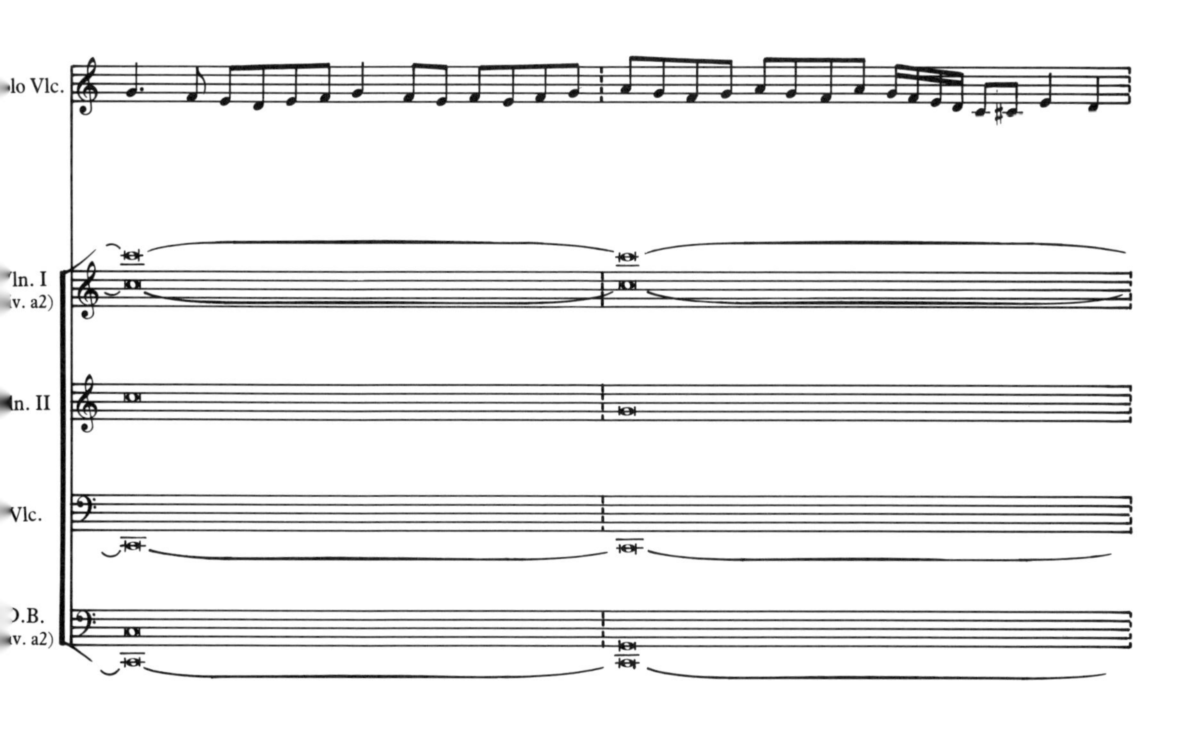
lo Vlc.
Vln. I
iv. a2)
ln. II
Vlc.
D.B.
iv. a2)

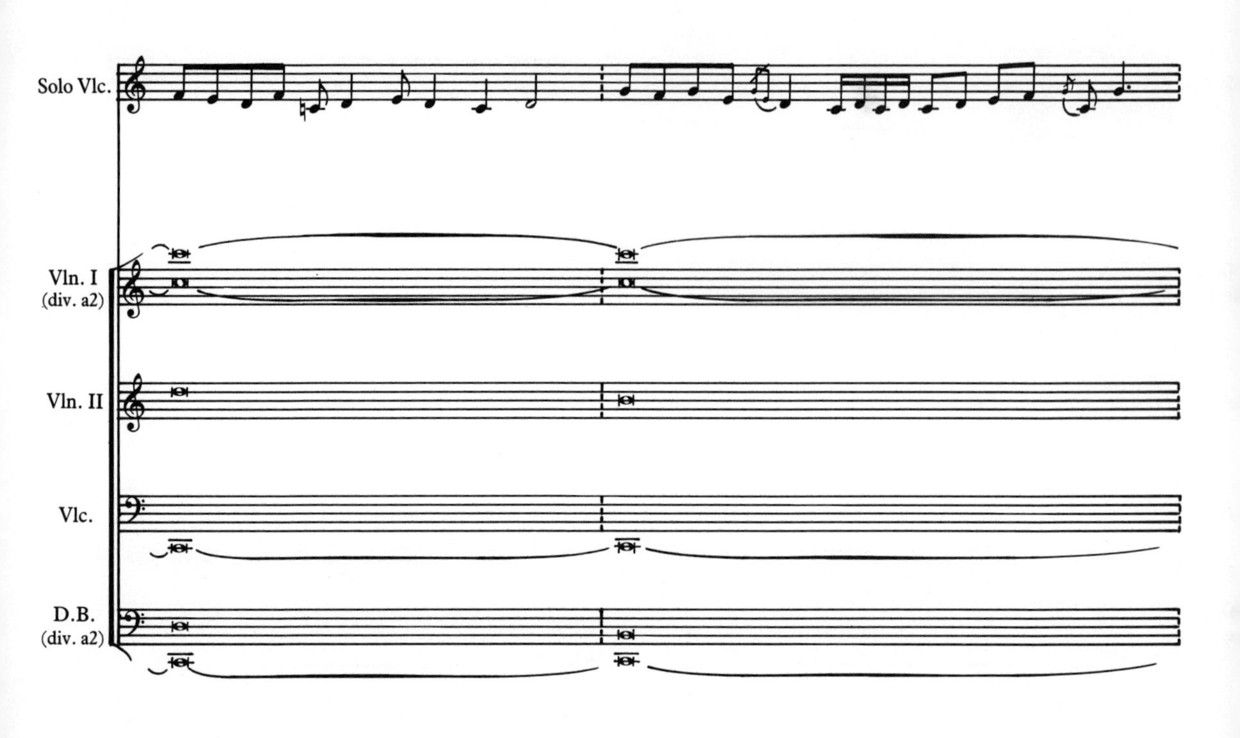
Solo Vlc.
Vln. I
(div. a2)
Vln. II
Vlc.
D.B.
(div. a2)

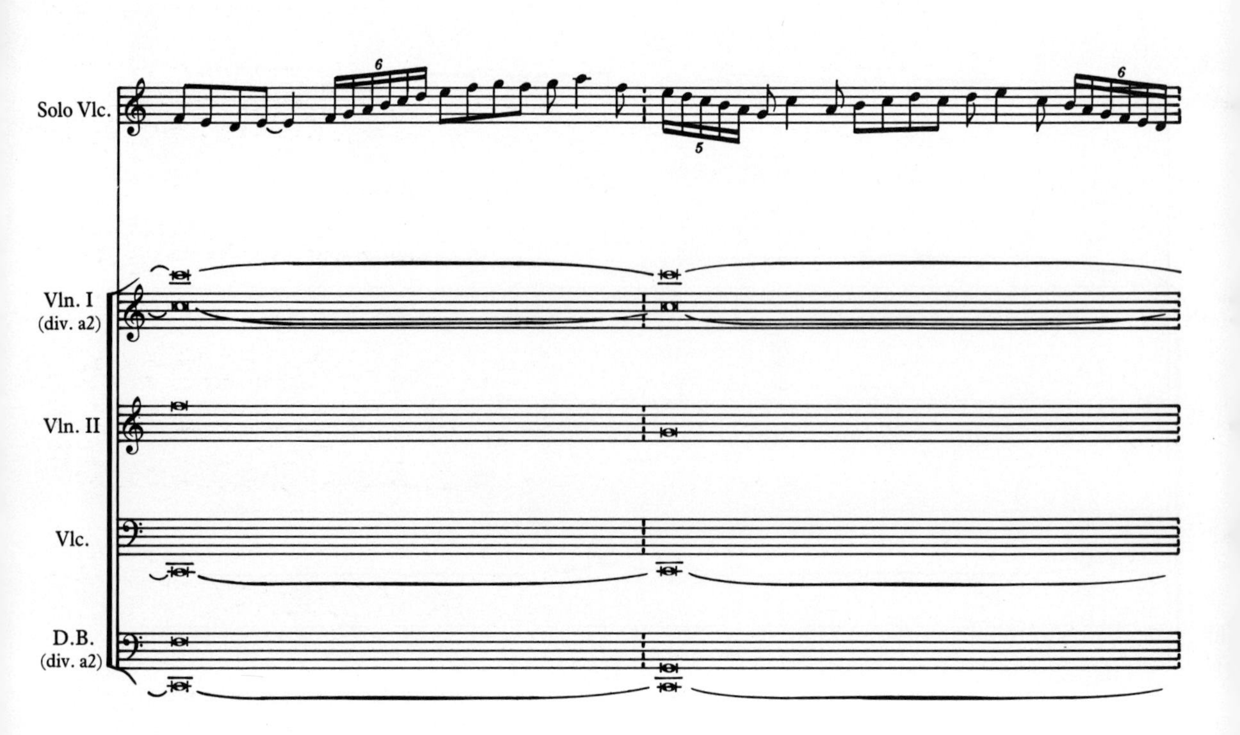
Solo Vlc.
6
5
6
Vln. I
(div. a2)
Vln. II
Vlc.
D.B.
(div. a2)

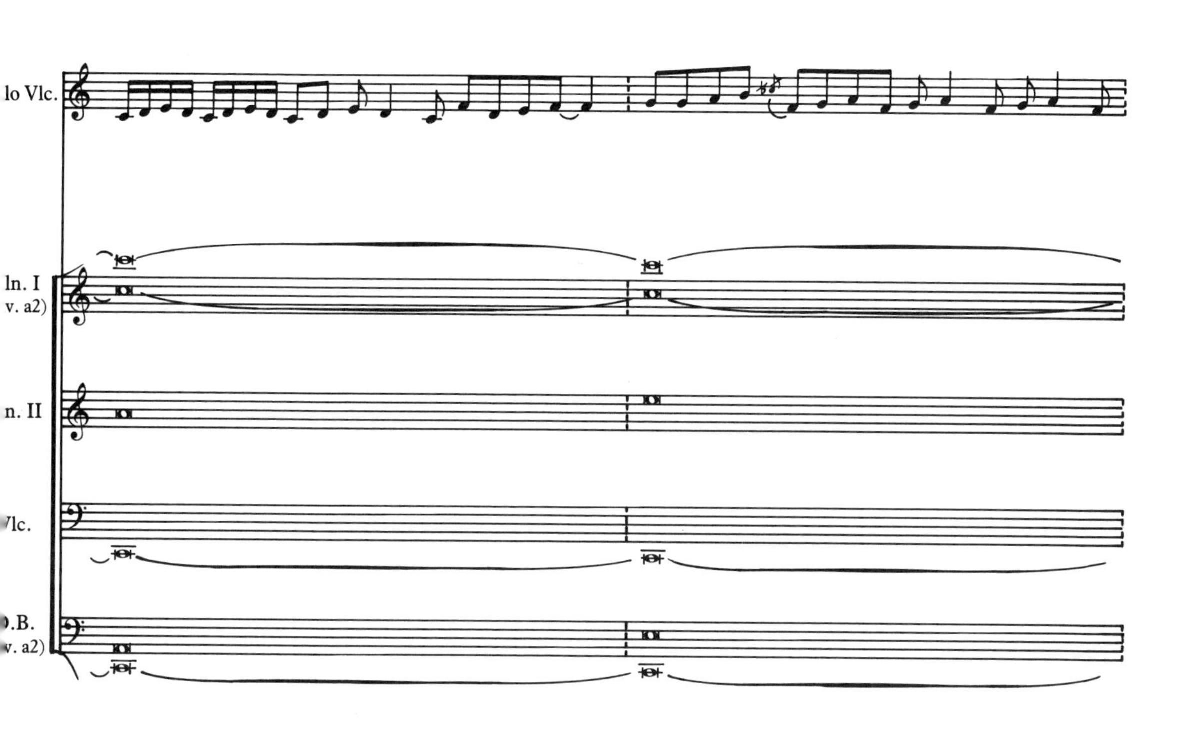
lo Vlc.
ln. I
v. a2)
n. II
Vlc.
B.
v. a2)

o Vlc.
n. I
. a2)
. II
c.
B.
. a2)

Solo Vlc.
Vln. I
(div. a2)
Vln. II
Vlc.
D.B.
(div. a2)

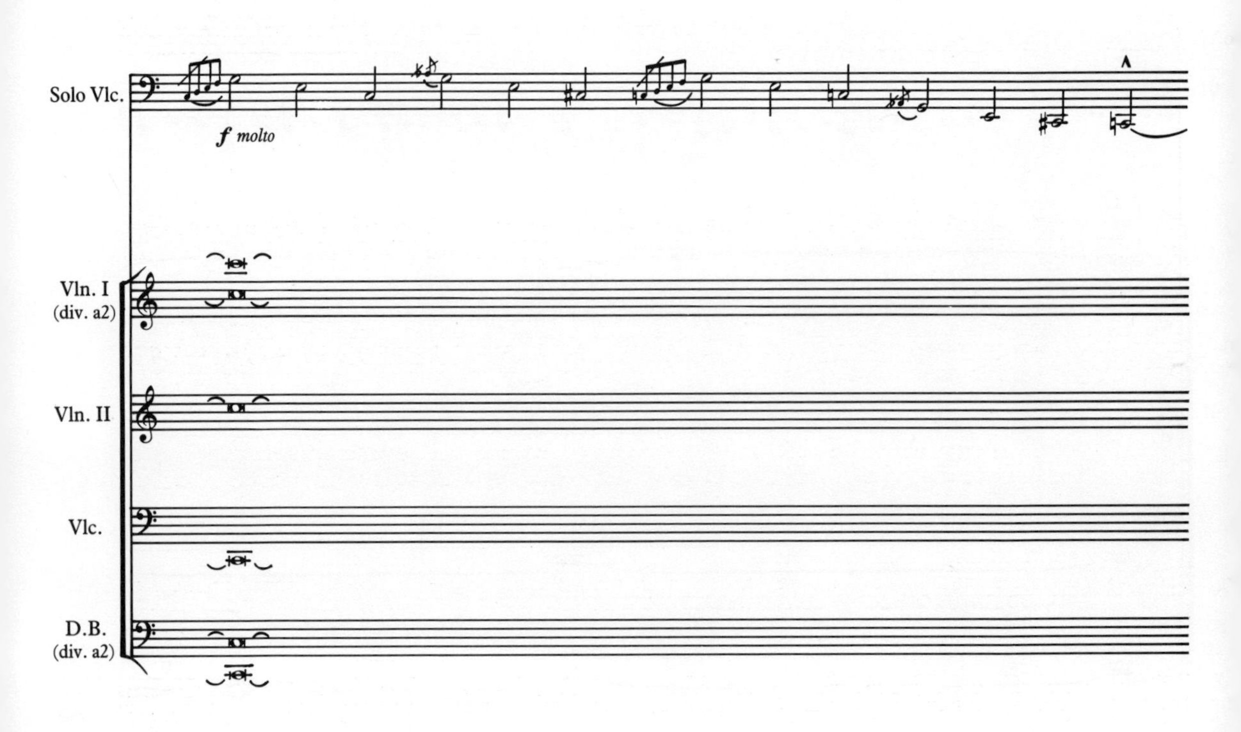
Solo Vlc.
f molto
Vln. I
(div. a2)
Vln. II
Vlc.
D.B.
(div. a2)

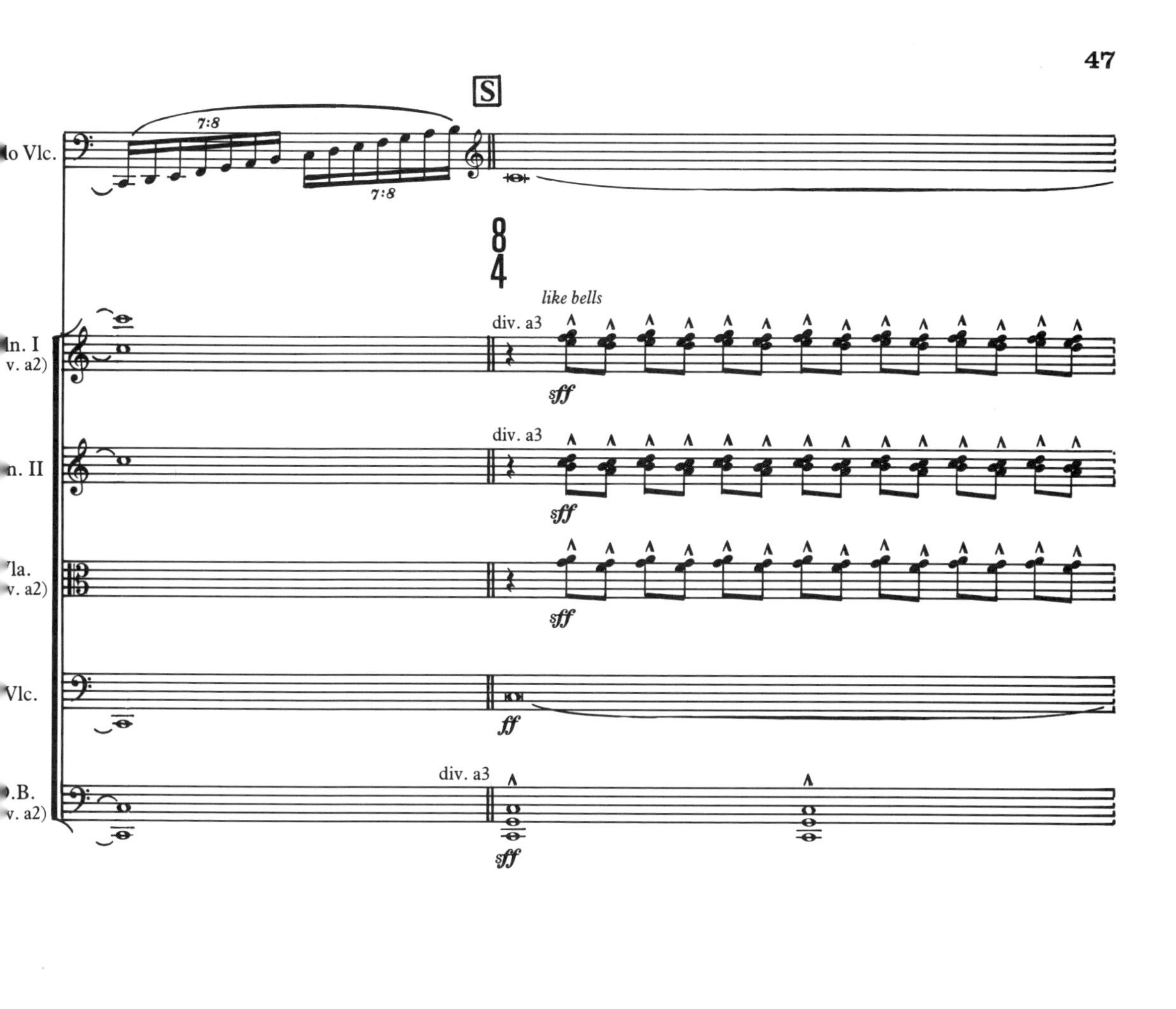
S
7:8
7:8
o Vlc.
8
4
like bells
div. a3
ln. I
v. a2)
sff
div. a3
n. II
sff
'la.
v. a2)
sff
Vlc.
ff
div. a3
.B.
v. a2)
sff

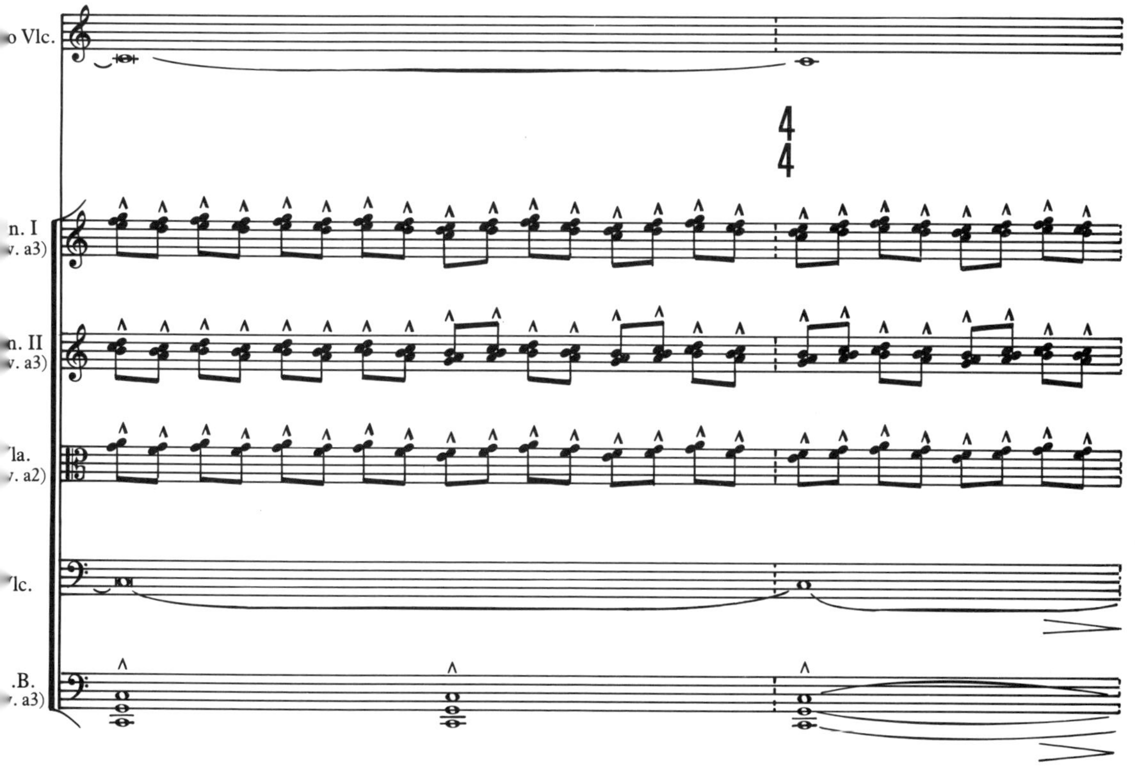
o Vlc.
4
4
n. I
v. a3)
n. II
v. a3)
'la.
v. a2)
'lc.
.B.
v. a3)

Solo Vlc.
Vln. I
(div. a3)
sff
Vln. II
(div. a3)
sff
Vla.
(div. a2)
sff
Vlc.
pp
ff
pp
D.B.
(div. a3)
pp poss.
sff
pp
Solo Vlc.
marcatiss.
Vln. I
(div. a3)
sff
Vln. II
(div. a3)
sff
Vla.
(div. a2)
sff
Vlc.
ff
pp
D.B.
(div. a3)
sff
pp

lo Vlc.
Vln. I
(div. a3)
sff
Vln. II
(div. a3)
sff
Vla.
(div. a2)
sff
Vlc.
ff
pp
D.B.
(div. a3)
sff
pp
lo Vlc.
Vln. I
(div. a3)
sff
Vln. II
(div. a3)
sff
Vla.
(div. a2)
sff
Vlc.
ff
D.B.
(div. a3)
sff
pp

T
dolce
Solo Vlc.
espress. molto
p ma sempre espress.
Vln. I
mp
Vlc.
(div. a2)
mp
mp sonore
D.B.
mp sonore
gently

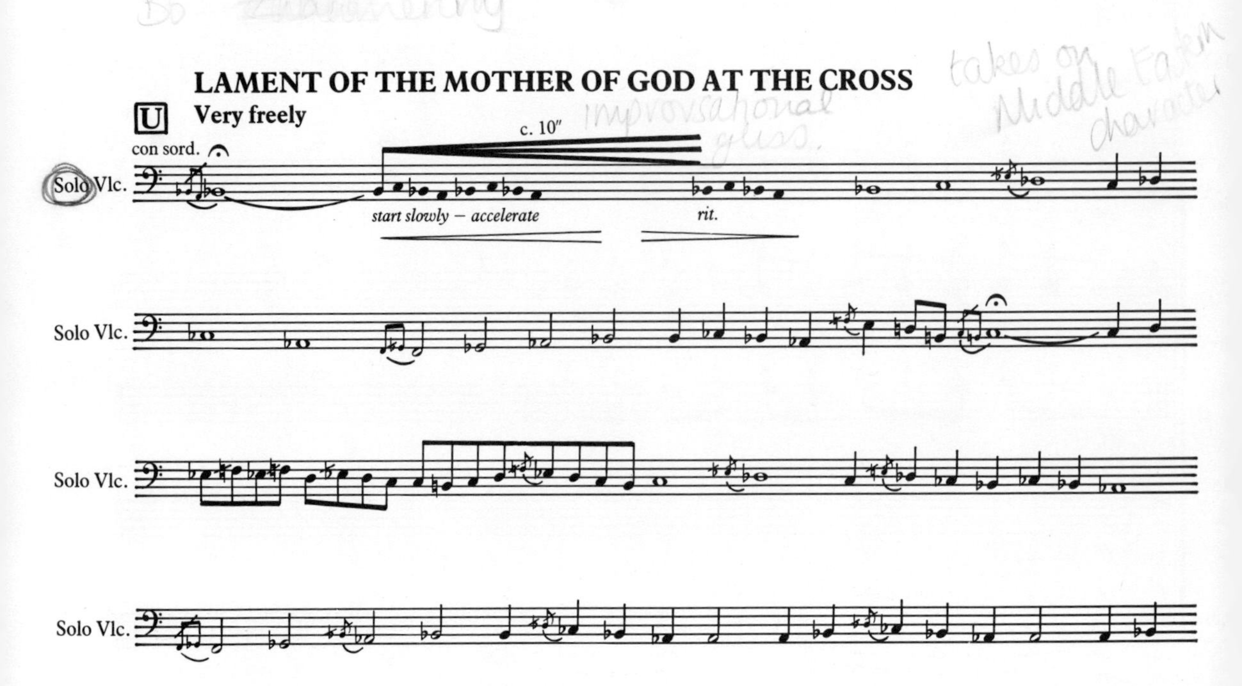
LAMENT OF THE MOTHER OF GOD AT THE CROSS
U
Very freely
con sord.
c. 10″
Solo Vlc.
start slowly – accelerate
rit.

lo Vlc.
c. 10″
start slowly – accelerate
rit.
pp
lunga
Slow
L.P.

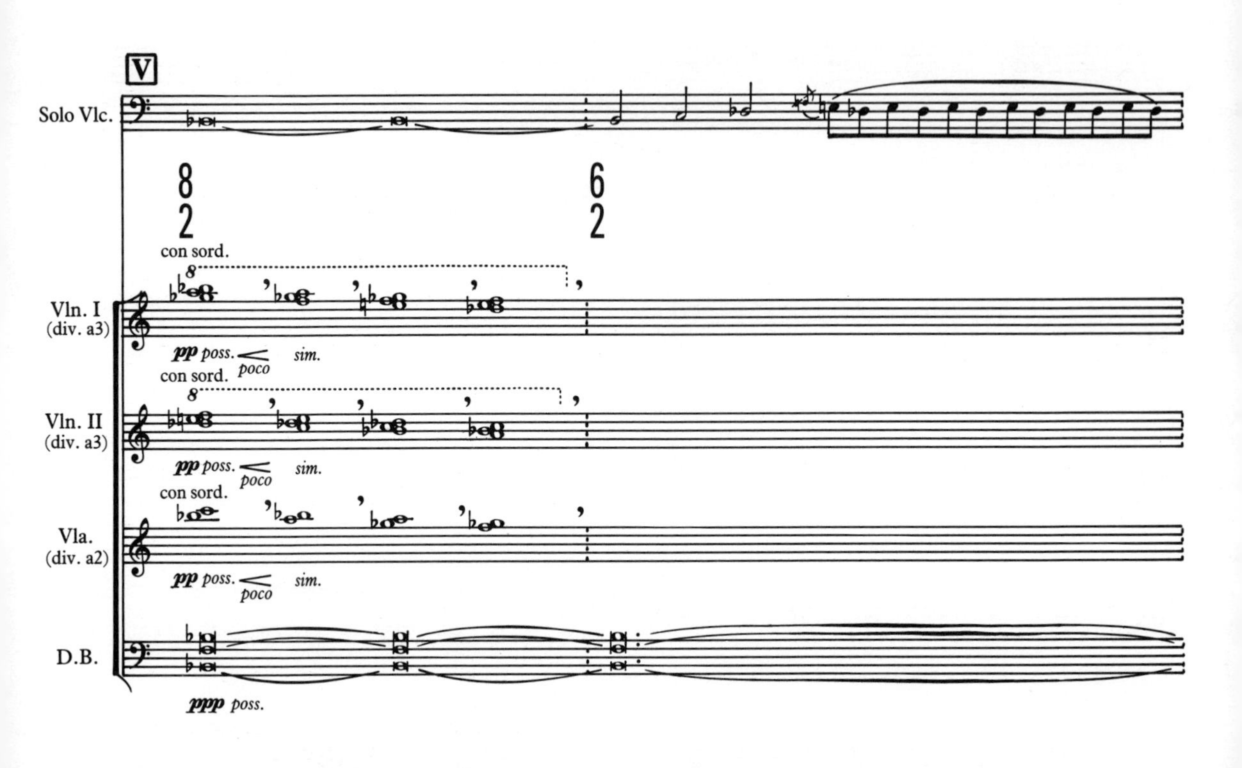
V
Solo Vlc.
8
2
6
2
con sord.
8
Vln. I
(div. a3)
pp poss.
poco
sim.
con sord.
8
Vln. II
(div. a3)
pp poss.
poco
sim.
con sord.
Vla.
(div. a2)
pp poss.
poco
sim.
D.B.
ppp poss.

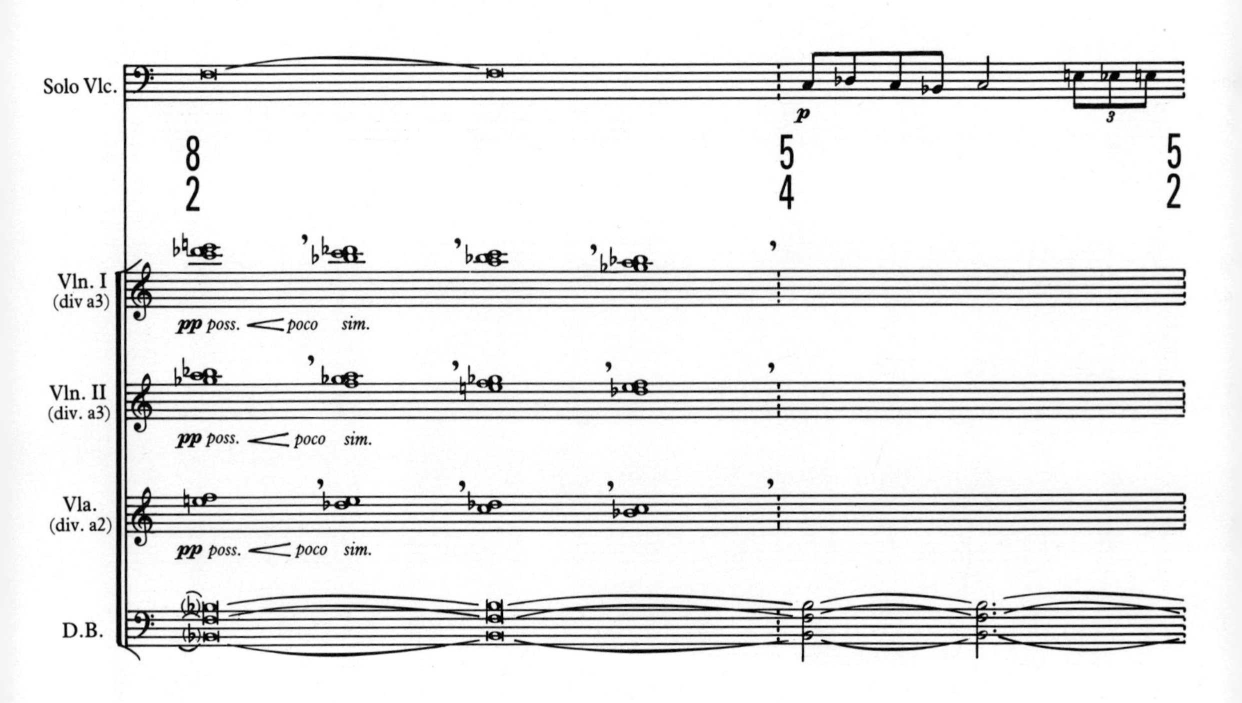
Solo Vlc.
p
3
8
2
5
4
5
2
Vln. I
(div a3)
pp poss.
poco
sim.
Vln. II
(div. a3)
pp poss.
poco
sim.
Vla.
(div. a2)
pp poss.
poco
sim.
D.B.

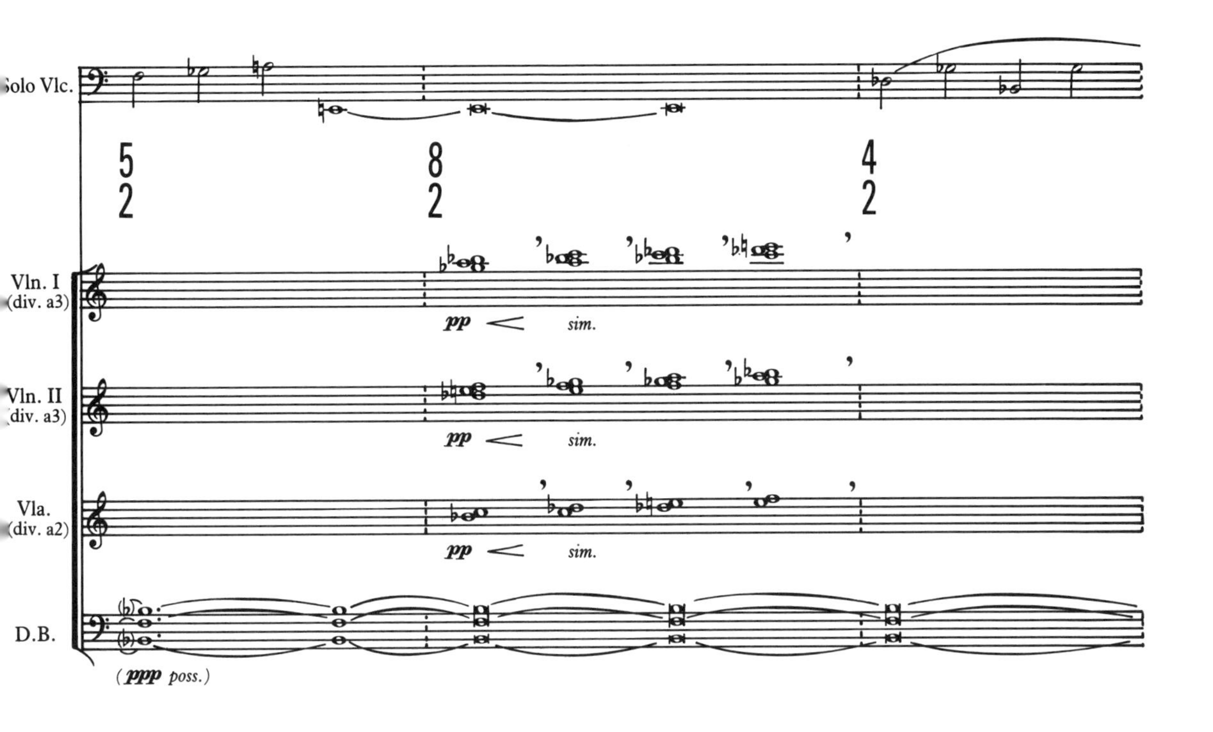
Solo Vlc.
5
2
8
2
4
2
Vln. I
(div. a3)
pp
sim.
Vln. II
(div. a3)
pp
sim.
Vla.
(div. a2)
pp
sim.
D.B.
(ppp poss.)

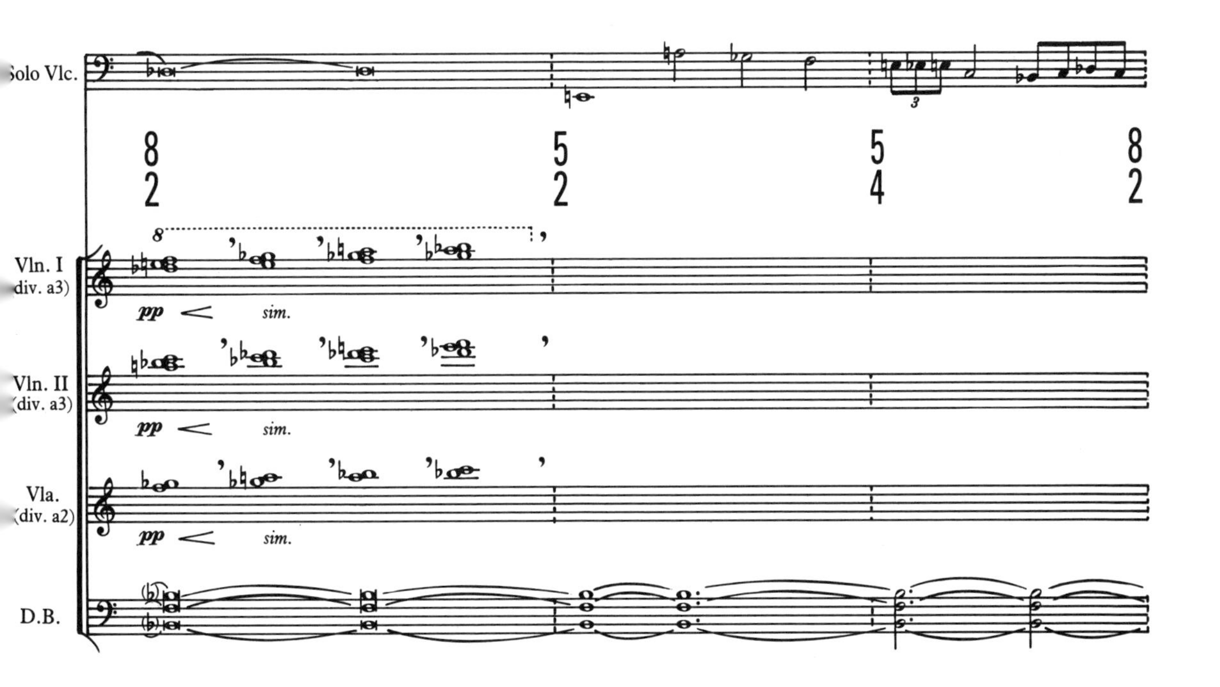
Solo Vlc.
3
8
2
5
2
5
4
8
2
Vln. I
(div. a3)
8
pp
sim.
Vln. II
(div. a3)
pp
sim.
Vla.
(div. a2)
pp
sim.
D.B.

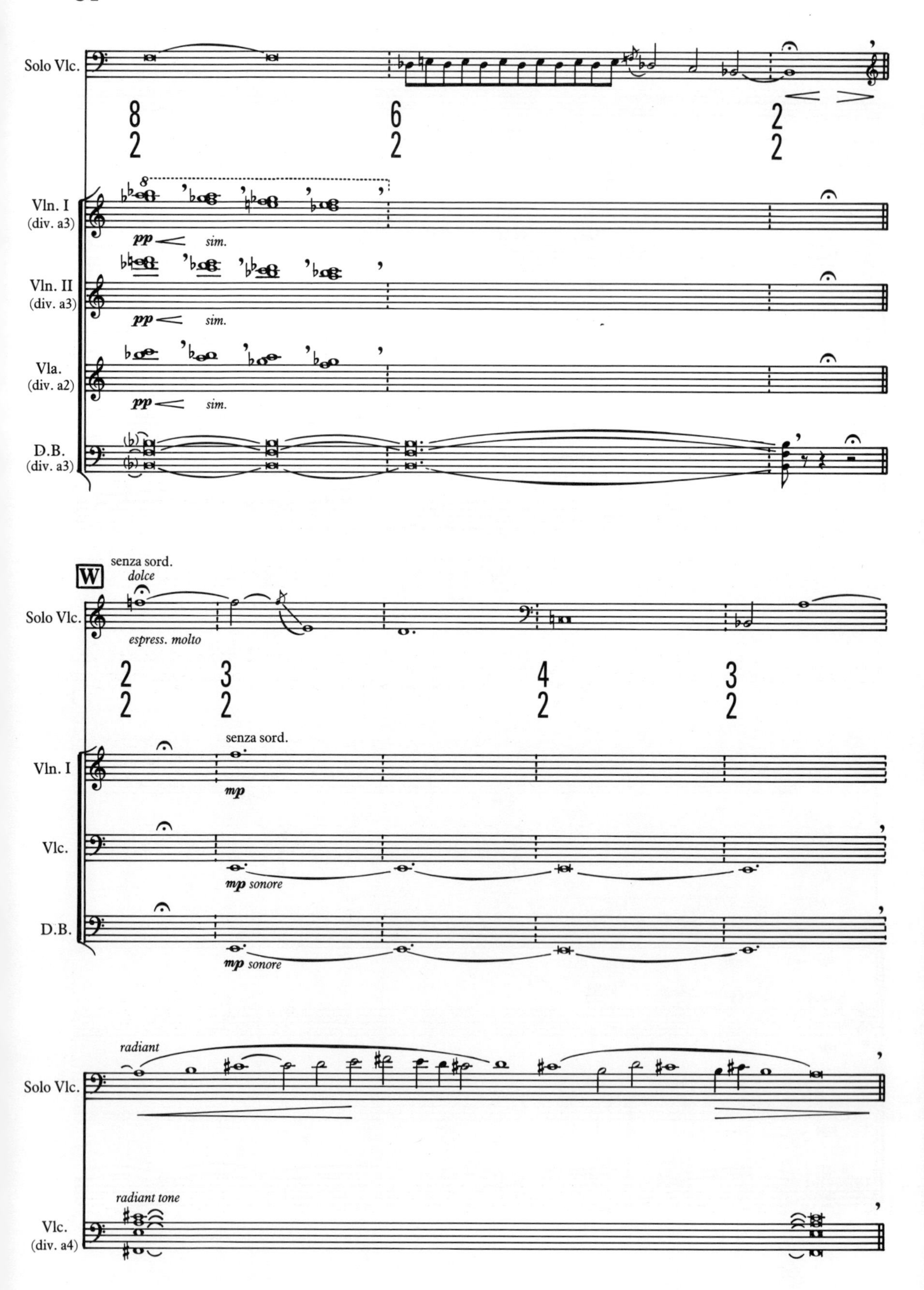
Solo Vlc.
Vln. I
(div. a3)
pp
sim.
Vln. II
(div. a3)
pp
sim.
Vla.
(div. a2)
pp
sim.
D.B.
(div. a3)
W
senza sord.
dolce
Solo Vlc.
espress. molto
senza sord.
Vln. I
mp
Vlc.
mp sonore
D.B.
mp sonore
radiant
Solo Vlc.
radiant tone
Vlc.
(div. a4)

CHRIST IS RISEN!
Always moving forward
X
sopra
Solo Vlc.
ff marcatiss.
3
Vln. I
(div.)
div.
f molto, marc.
f molto
Vln. II
(div.)
senza sord.
f molto
senza sord.
f molto
senza sord.
f molto
Vla.
(div. a4)
senza sord.
f molto
f molto
Vlc.
(div. a5)
f molto
f molto
D.B.
(div. a3)
f molto

Solo Vlc.
(div.)
Vln. I
(div.)
8
senza sord.
div.
f molto
Vln. II
(div.)
Vla.
(div. a4)
Vlc.
(div. a5)
D.B.
(div. a3)

olo Vlc.
4
2
9
4
4
2
(div.)
Vln. I
(div.)
(div.)
Vln. II
(div.)
Vla.
iv. a4)
Vlc.
iv. a5)
D.B.
div. a3)

Solo Vlc.
2
2
4
2
9
4
(div.)
Vln. I
(div.)
8
(div.)
Vln. II
(div.)
Vla.
(div. a4)
Vlc.
(div. a5)
D.B.
(div. a3)

Solo Vlc.
(div.)
Vln. I
(div.)
(div.)
Vln. II
(div.)
Vla.
div. a4)
Vlc.
iv. a5)
D.B.
div. a3)

Y
Solo Vlc.
ff
like bells
sim.
Vln. I
(div. a3)
sff
sim.
Vln. II
(div. a3)
sff
sim.
Vla.
(div. a2)
sff
D.B.
(div. a3)
sff

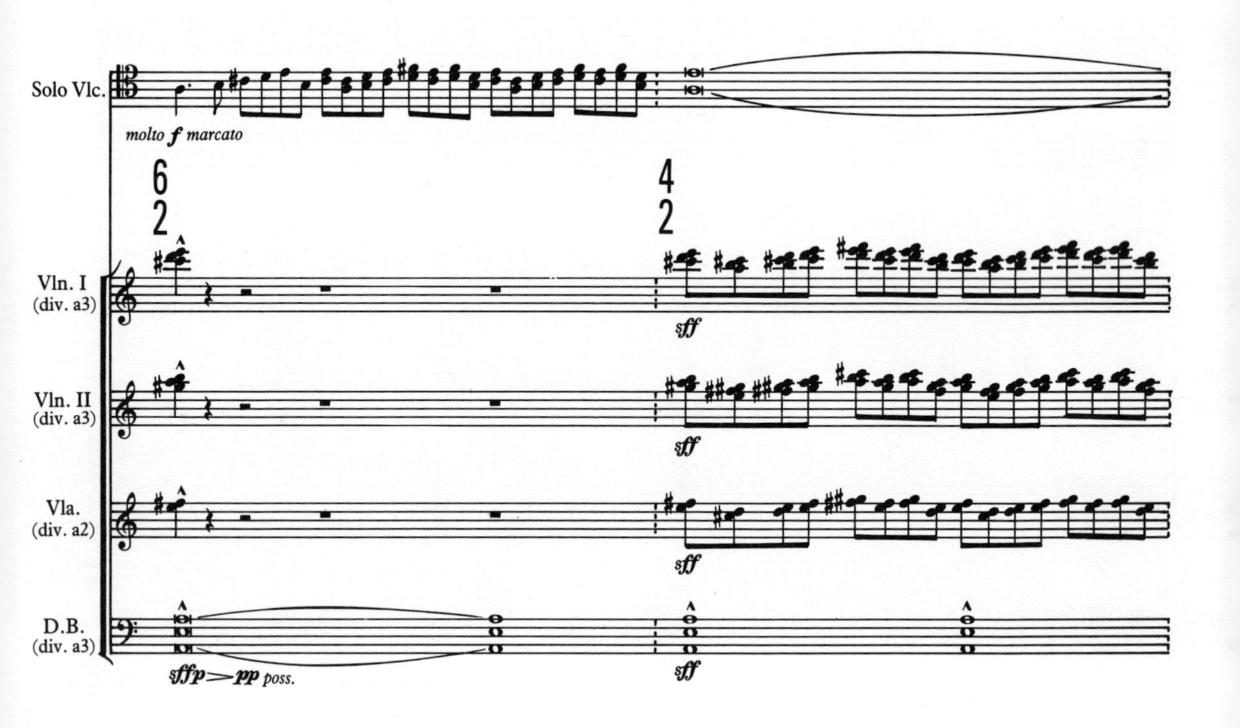
Solo Vlc.
molto f marcato
Vln. I
(div. a3)
sff
Vln. II
(div. a3)
sff
Vla.
(div. a2)
sff
D.B.
(div. a3)
sffp > pp poss.
sff

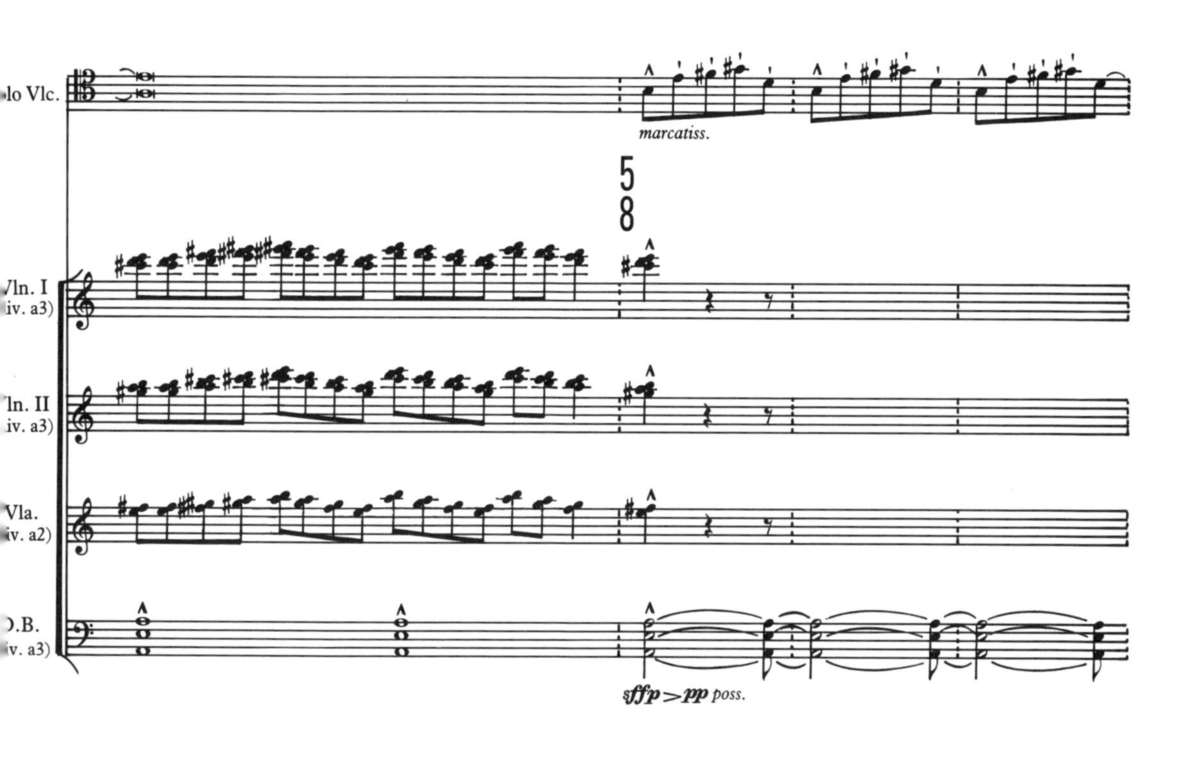
lo Vlc.
marcatiss.
5
8
Vln. I
iv. a3)
ln. II
iv. a3)
Vla.
iv. a2)
D.B.
iv. a3)
sffp > pp poss.

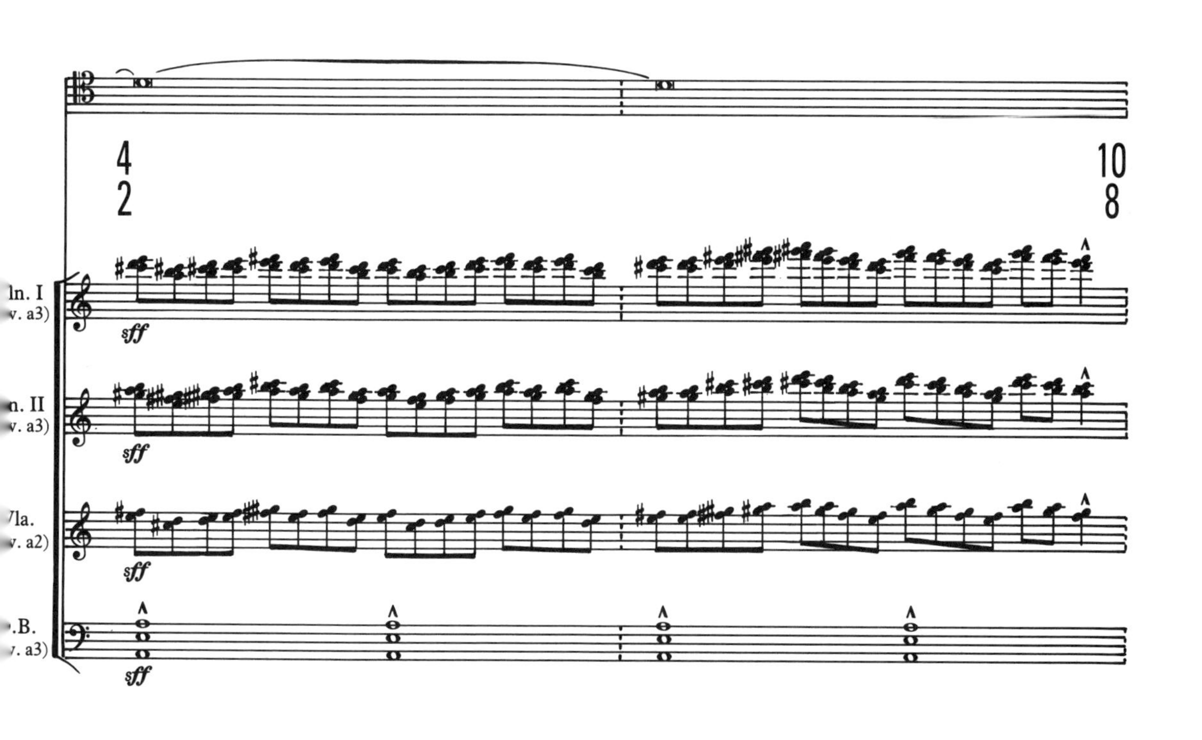
4
2
10
8
ln. I
v. a3)
sff
n. II
v. a3)
sff
Vla.
v. a2)
sff
.B.
v. a3)
sff

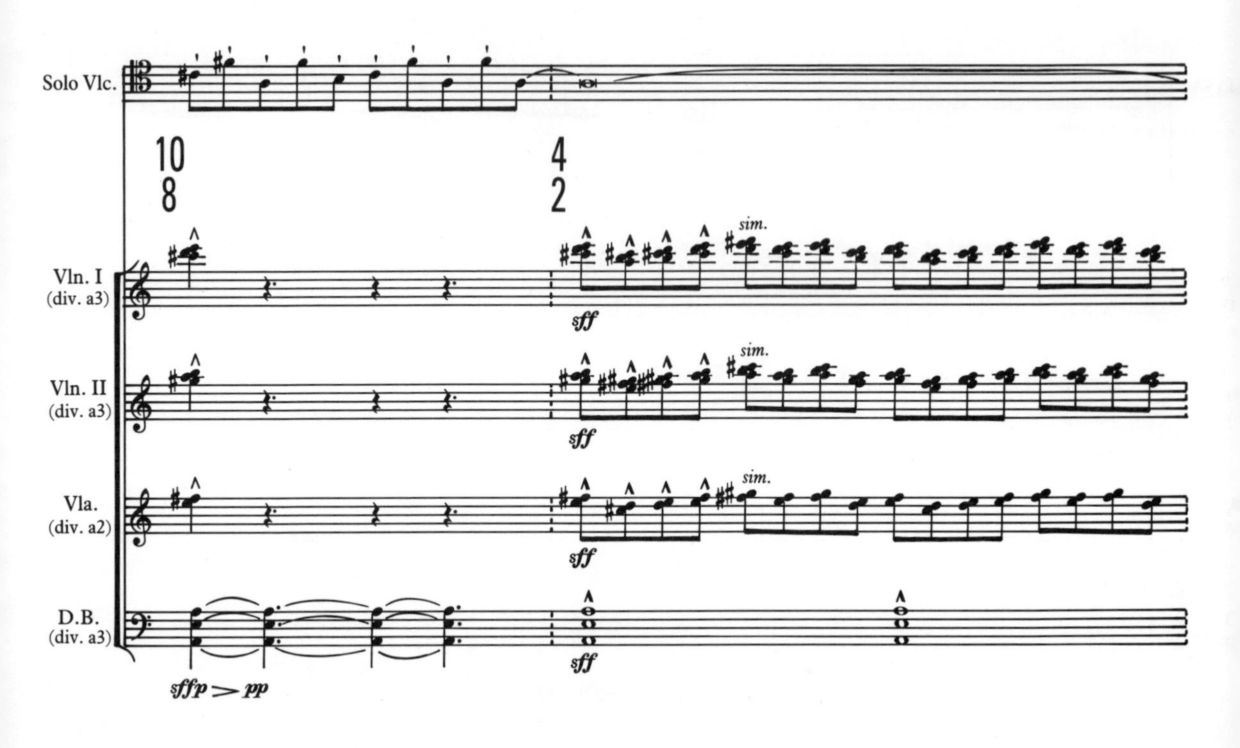
Solo Vlc.
10
8
4
2
Vln. I
(div. a3)
sim.
sff
Vln. II
(div. a3)
sim.
sff
Vla.
(div. a2)
sim.
sff
D.B.
(div. a3)
sff
sffp > pp

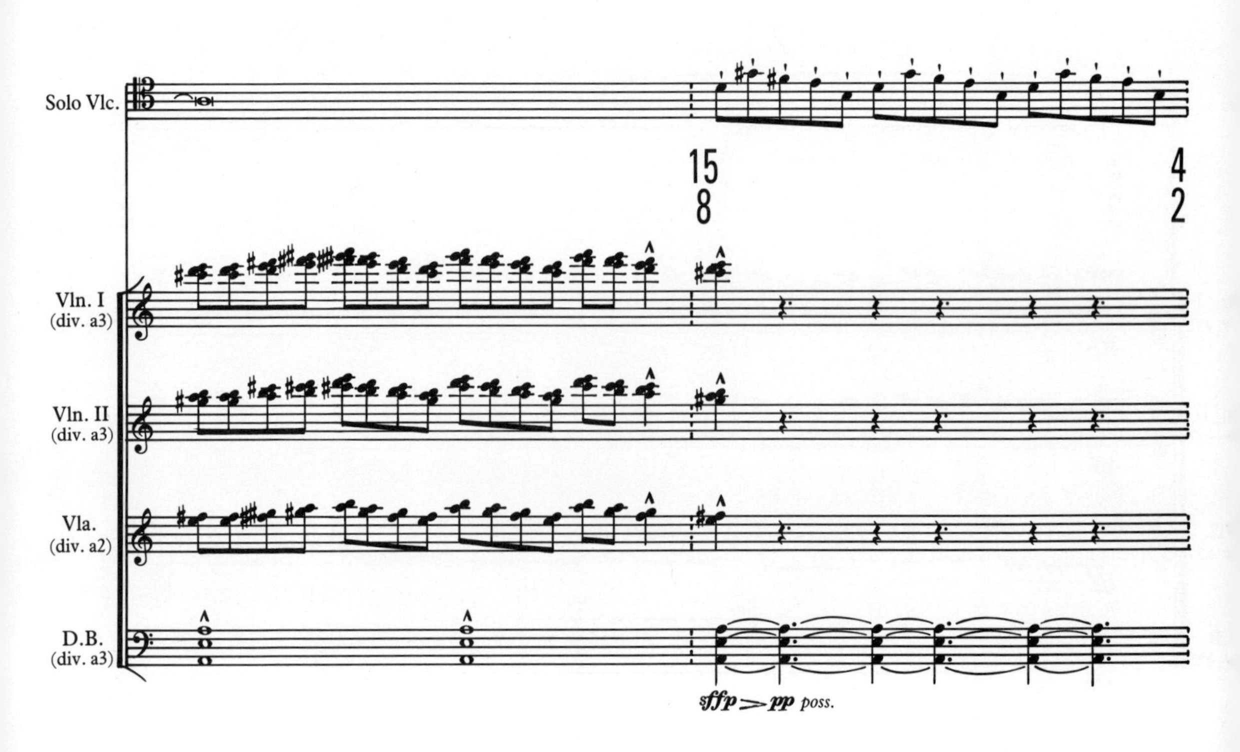
Solo Vlc.
15
8
4
2
Vln. I
(div. a3)
Vln. II
(div. a3)
Vla.
(div. a2)
D.B.
(div. a3)
sffp > pp poss.

lo Vlc.
4
2
ln. I
v. a3)
sff
n. II
v. a3)
sff
Vla.
v. a2)
sff
).B.
v. a3)
sff

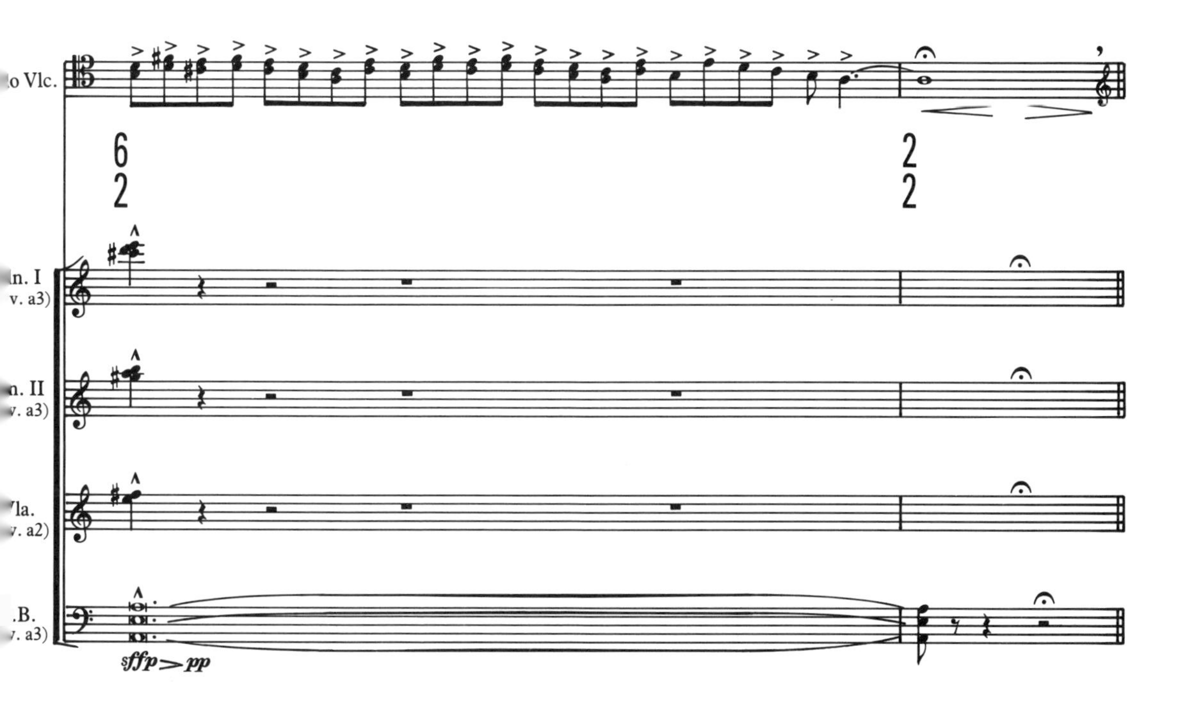
lo Vlc.
6
2
2
2
ln. I
v. a3)
n. II
v. a3)
Vla.
v. a2)
.B.
v. a3)
sffp > pp

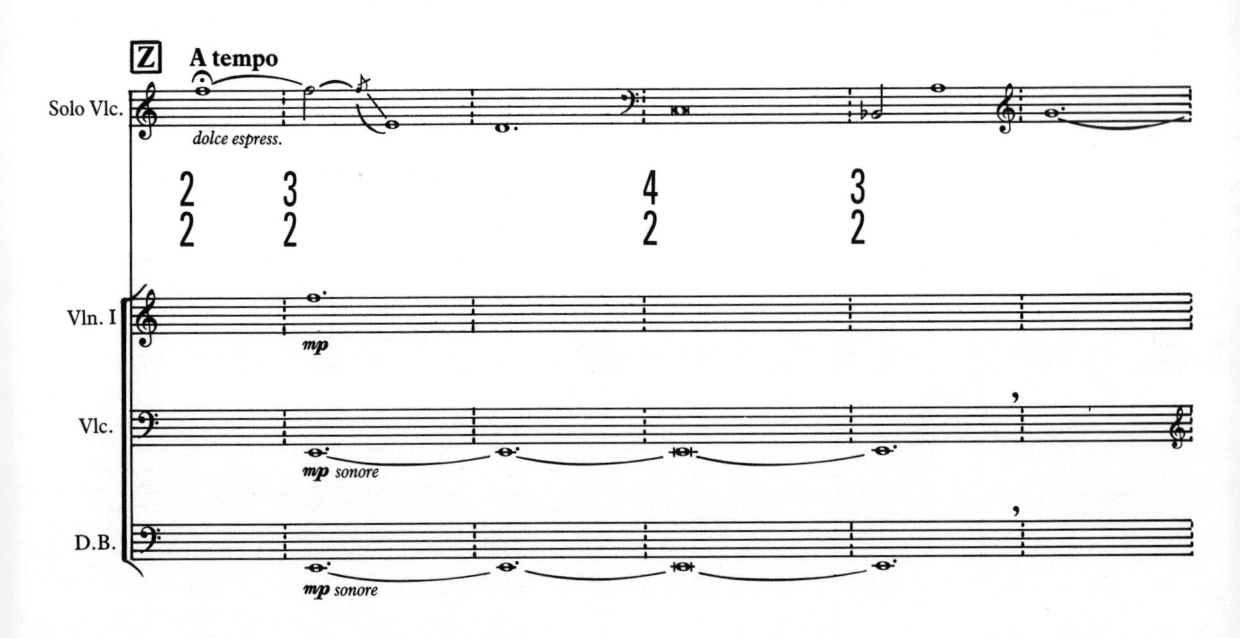
Z
A tempo
Solo Vlc.
dolce espress.
2
2
3
2
4
2
3
2
Vln. I
mp
Vlc.
mp sonore
D.B.
mp sonore

molto espress.
Solo Vlc.
solo
Vlc.

THE DORMITION OF THE MOTHER OF GOD

AA **Much slower**

Quiet, solemn and tender, with a broad flowing line

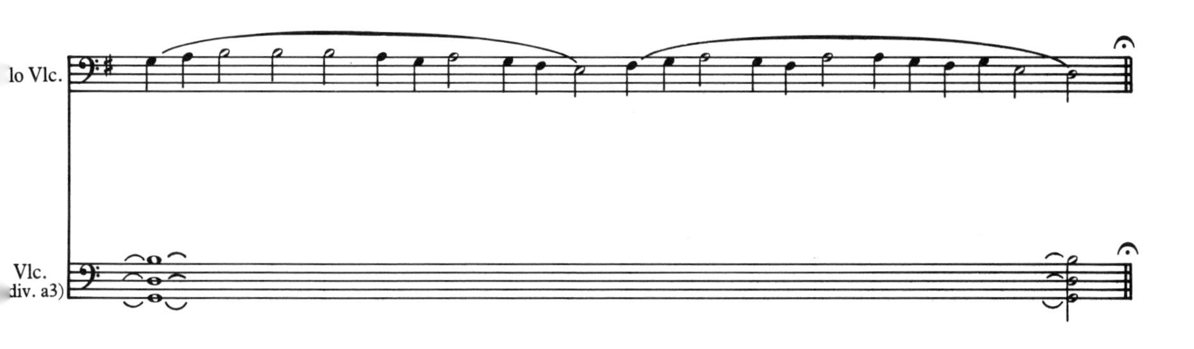

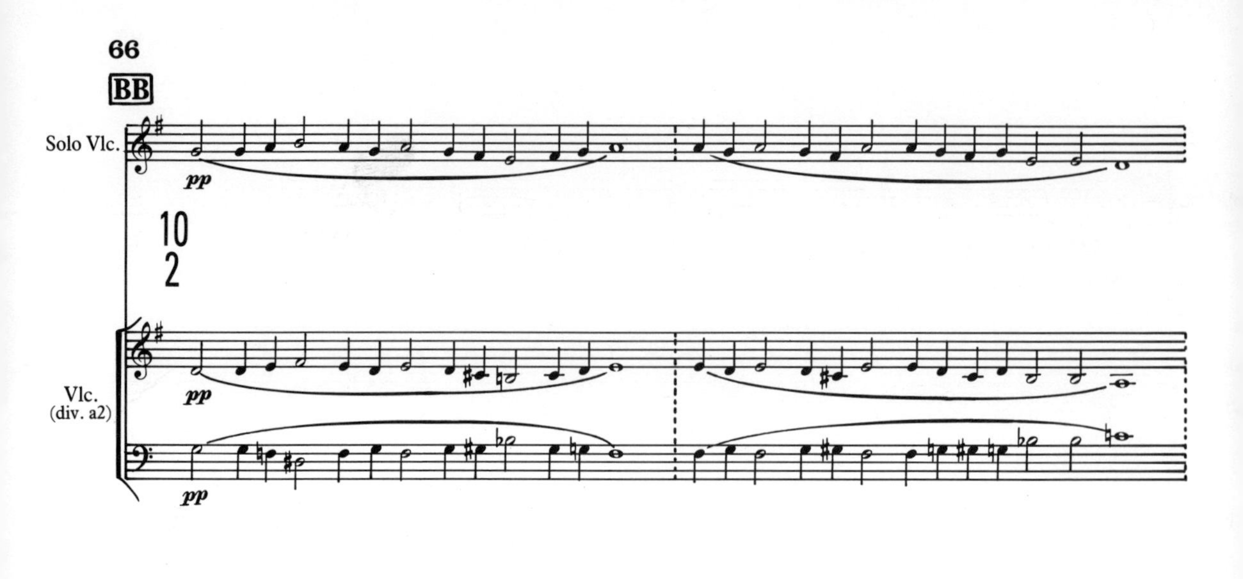
BB
Solo Vlc.
pp
10
2
Vlc.
(div. a2)
pp
pp

Solo Vlc.
9
2
8
2
Vlc.
(div. a2)

Solo Vlc.
9
2
11
2
10
2
Vlc.
(div. a2)

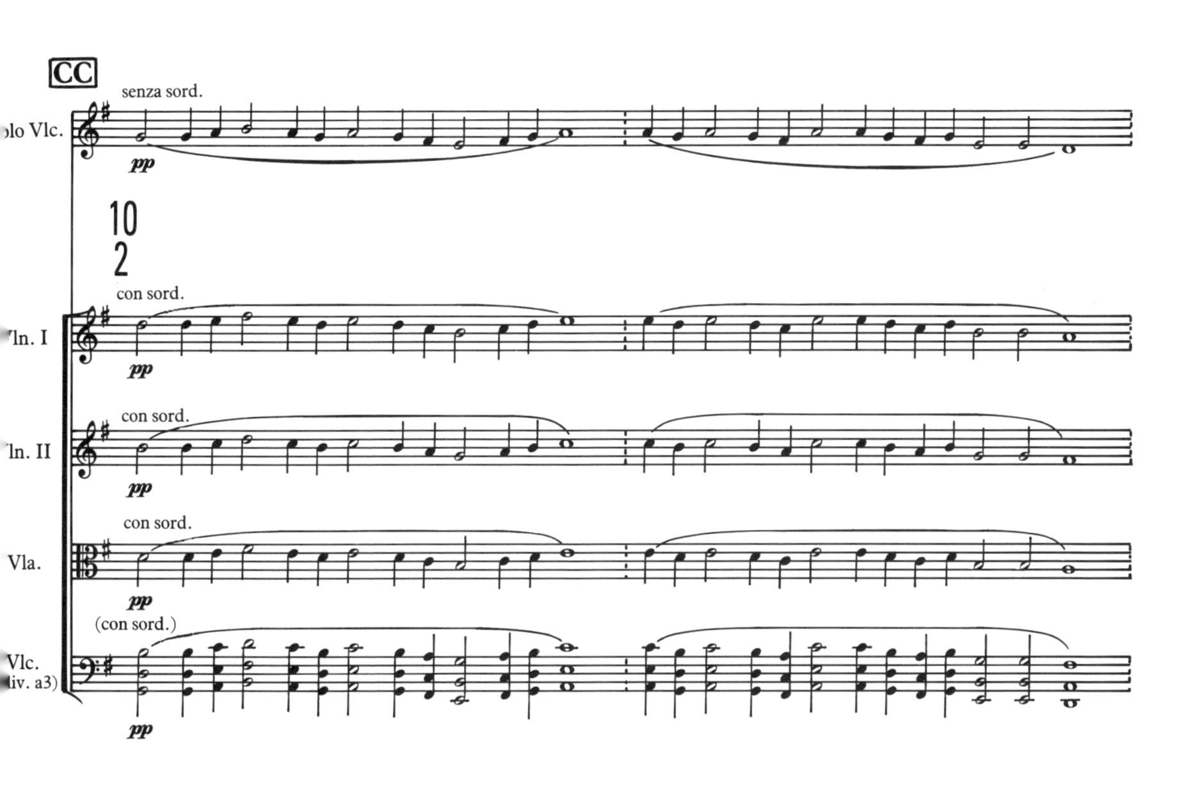
CC
senza sord.
olo Vlc.
pp
10
2
con sord.
Vln. I
pp
con sord.
Vln. II
pp
con sord.
Vla.
pp
(con sord.)
Vlc.
(div. a3)
pp

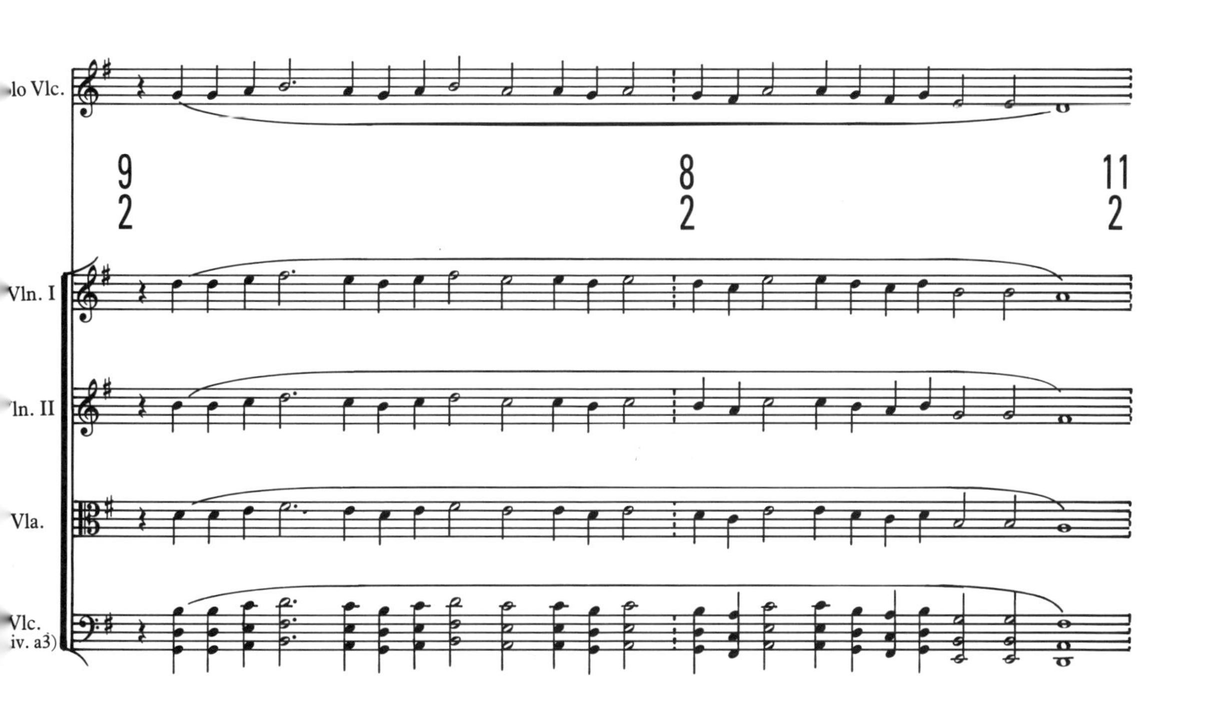
olo Vlc.
9
2
8
2
11
2
Vln. I
Vln. II
Vla.
Vlc.
(div. a3)

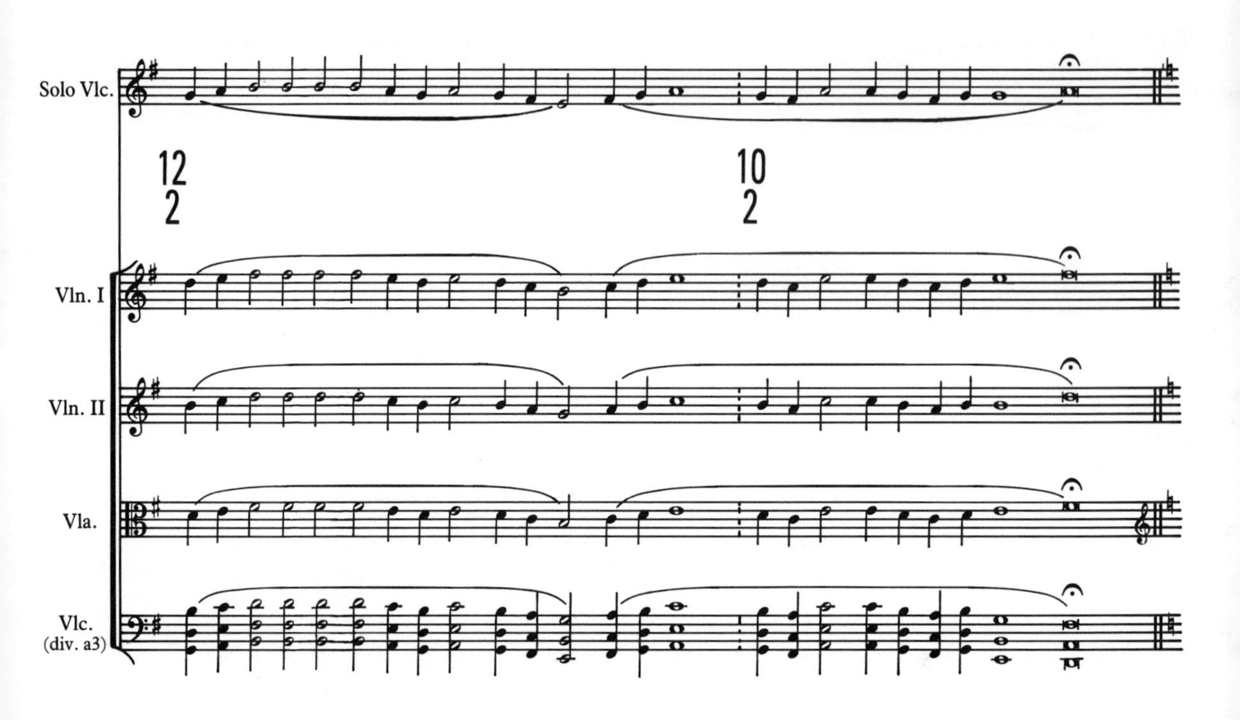
Solo Vlc.
12
2
10
2
Vln. I
Vln. II
Vla.
Vlc.
(div. a3)

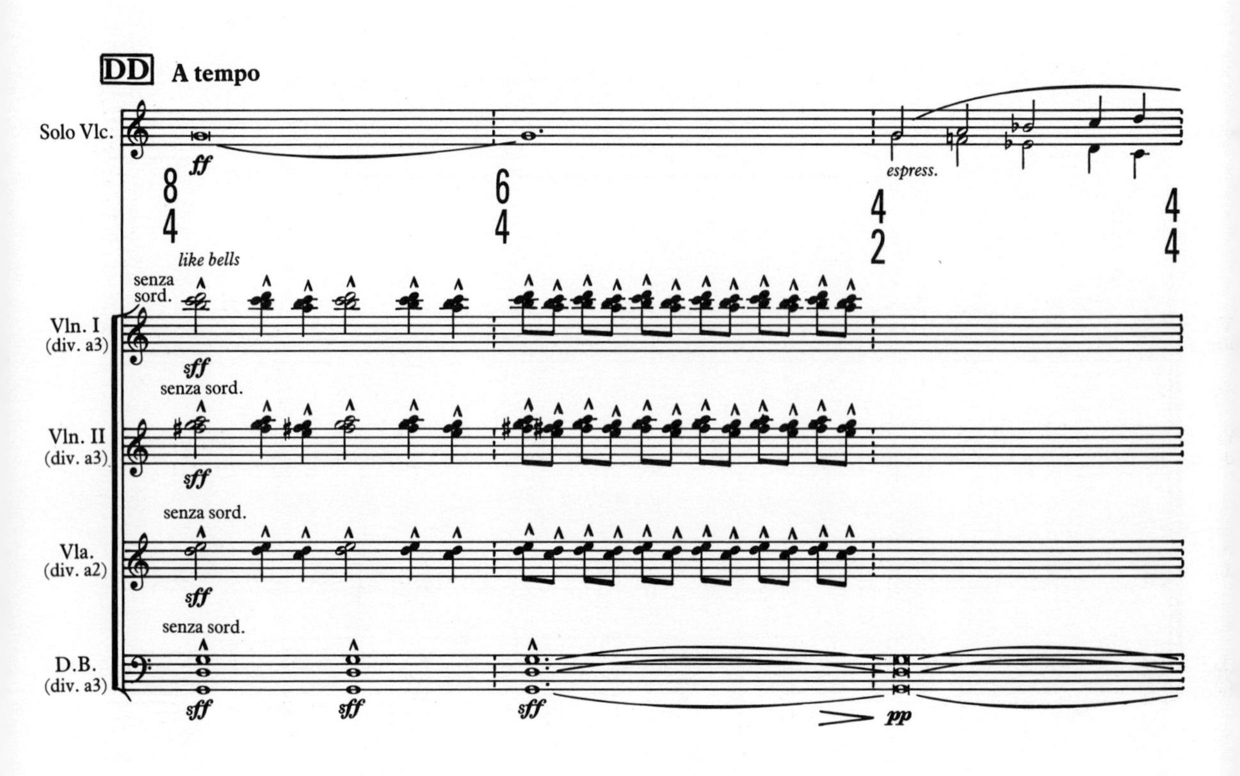
DD
A tempo
Solo Vlc.
ff
espress.
8
4
6
4
4
2
4
4
like bells
senza sord.
Vln. I
(div. a3)
sff
senza sord.
Vln. II
(div. a3)
sff
senza sord.
Vla.
(div. a2)
sff
senza sord.
D.B.
(div. a3)
sff
sff
sff
pp

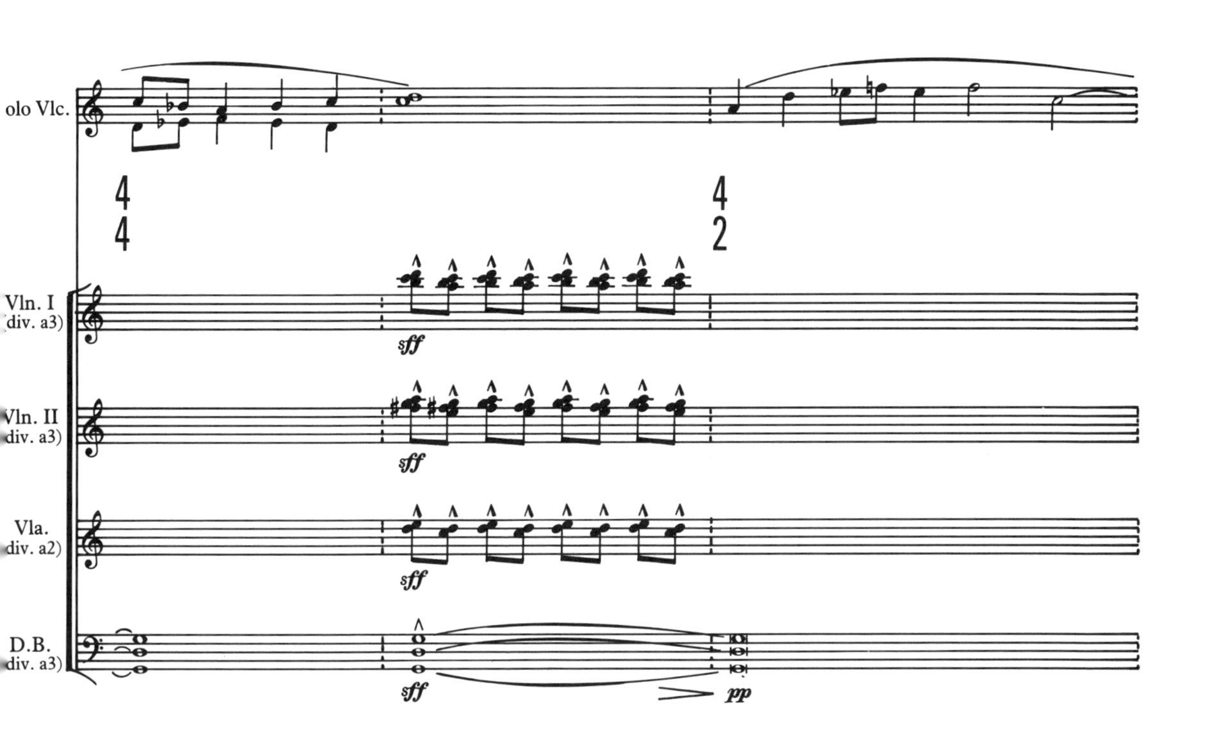
olo Vlc.
Vln. I
div. a3)
sff
Vln. II
div. a3)
sff
Vla.
div. a2)
sff
D.B.
div. a3)
sff
pp

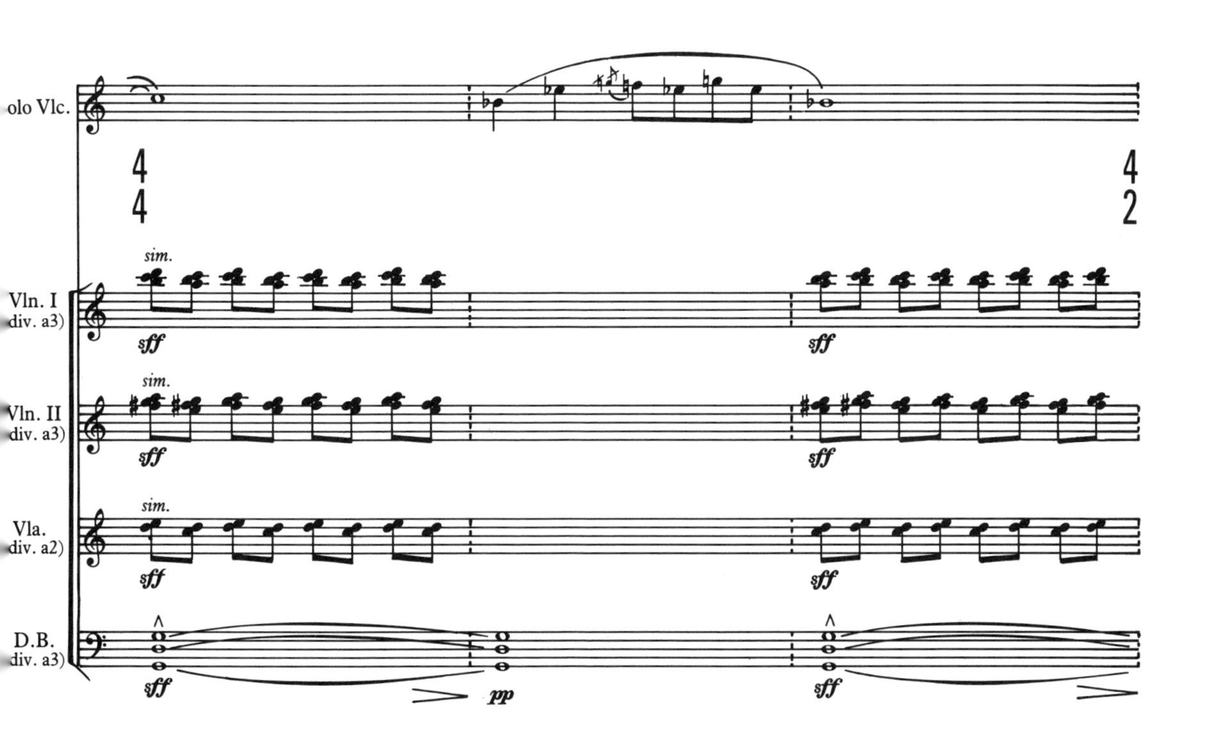
olo Vlc.
sim.
Vln. I
div. a3)
sff
sff
sim.
Vln. II
div. a3)
sff
sff
sim.
Vla.
div. a2)
sff
sff
D.B.
div. a3)
sff
pp
sff

Solo Vlc.
Vln. I
(div. a3)
sff
Vln. II
(div. a3)
sff
Vla.
(div. a2)
sff
D.B.
(div. a3)
pp
sff
pp

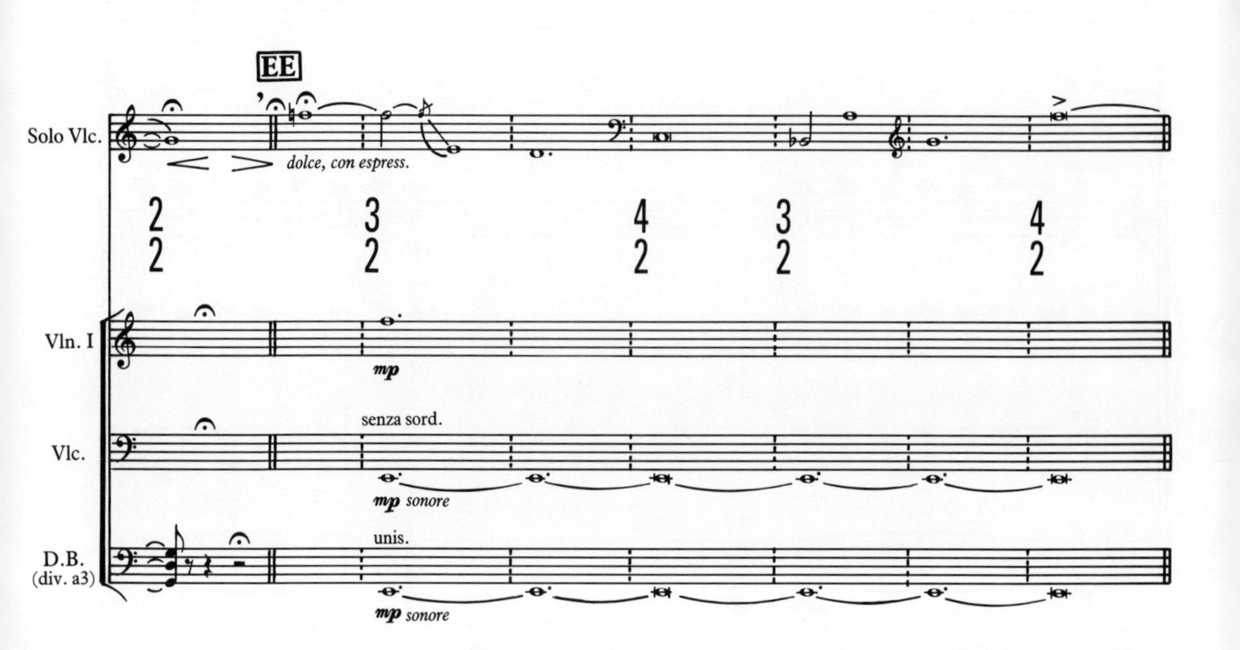
EE
Solo Vlc.
dolce, con espress.
Vln. I
mp
senza sord.
Vlc.
mp sonore
unis.
D.B.
(div. a3)
mp sonore

THE PROTECTING VEIL

Transcendent, with awesome majesty

olo Vlc. *f molto*

Vln. I *niente* *molto*

Vln. II *niente* *molto*

Vla. *niente* *molto*

Vlc. (iv. a3) *niente* *molto* *niente* *molto* *niente* *molto*

).B. (iv. a3) *niente* *molto* *niente* *molto* *niente* *molto*

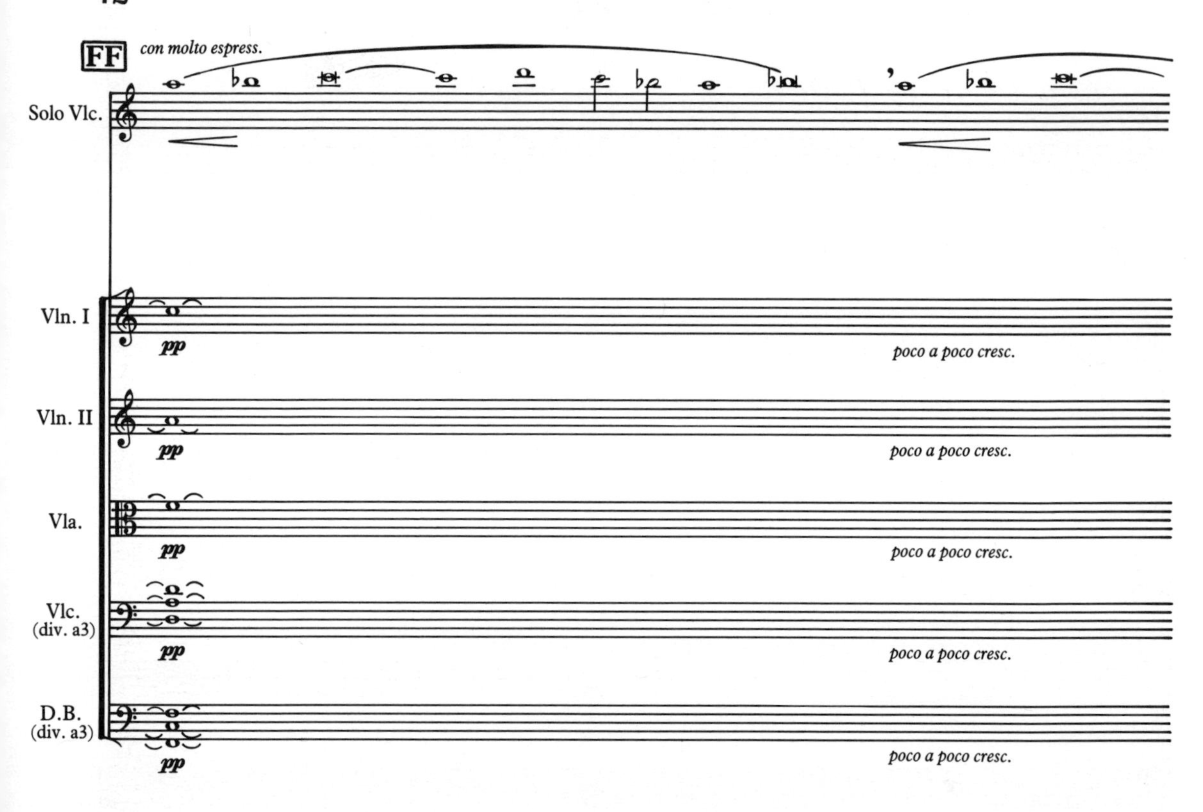
FF
con molto espress.
Solo Vlc.
Vln. I
pp
poco a poco cresc.
Vln. II
pp
poco a poco cresc.
Vla.
pp
poco a poco cresc.
Vlc.
(div. a3)
pp
poco a poco cresc.
D.B.
(div. a3)
pp
poco a poco cresc.

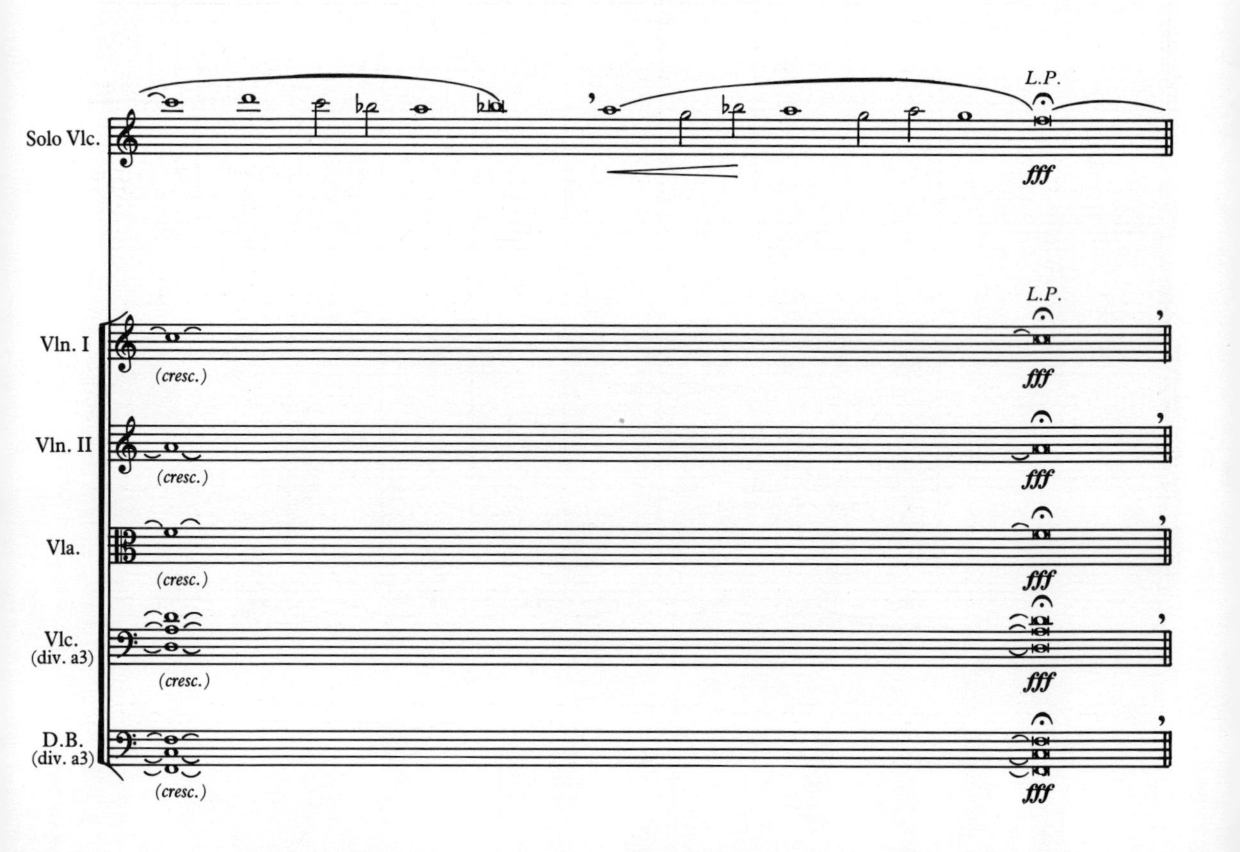
L.P.
Solo Vlc.
fff
L.P.
Vln. I
(cresc.)
fff
Vln. II
(cresc.)
fff
Vla.
(cresc.)
fff
Vlc.
(div. a3)
(cresc.)
fff
D.B.
(div. a3)
(cresc.)
fff

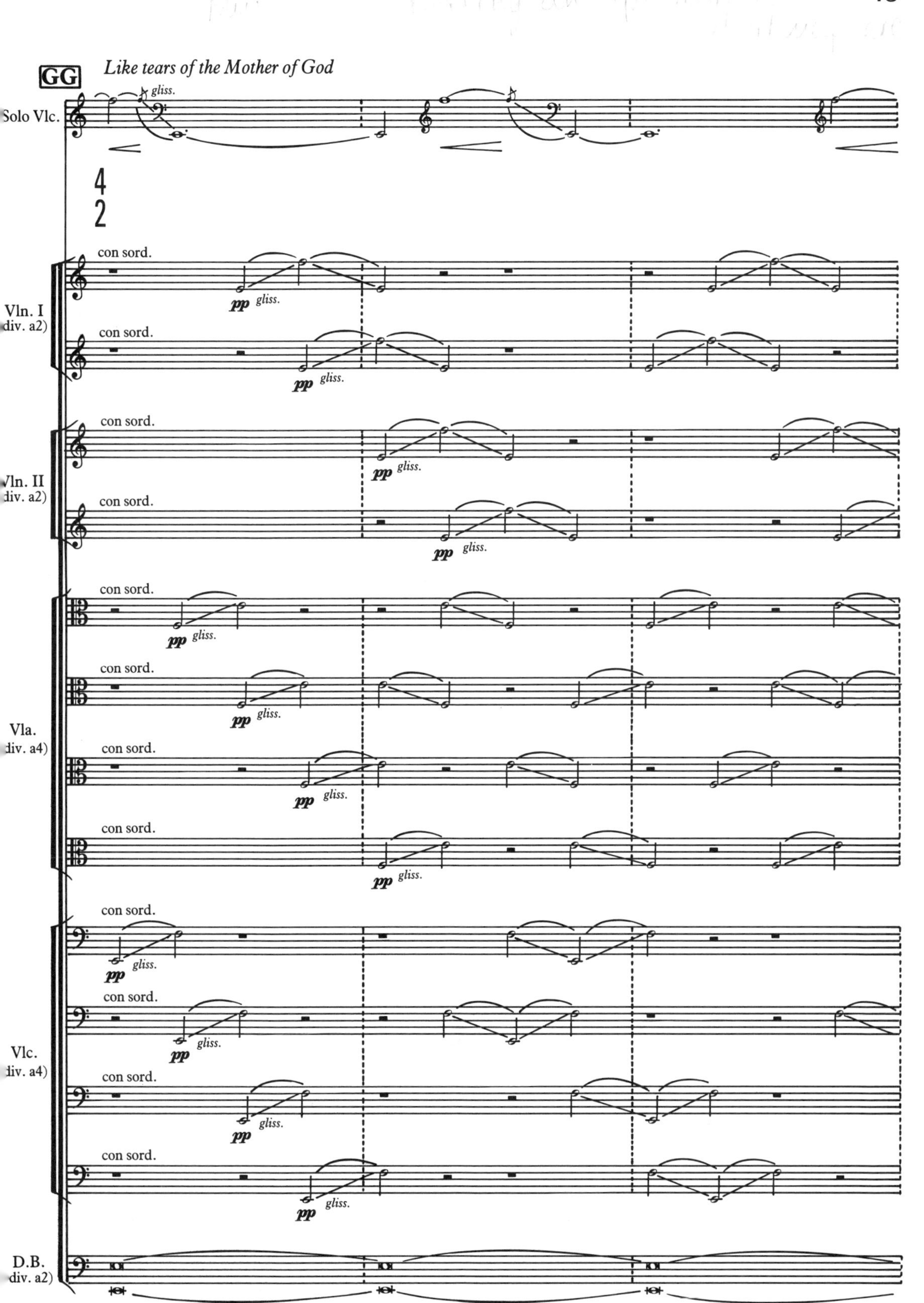
GG
Like tears of the Mother of God
gliss.
Solo Vlc.
con sord.
pp gliss.
Vln. I
(div. a2)
Vln. II
(div. a2)
Vla.
(div. a4)
Vlc.
(div. a4)
D.B.
(div. a2)

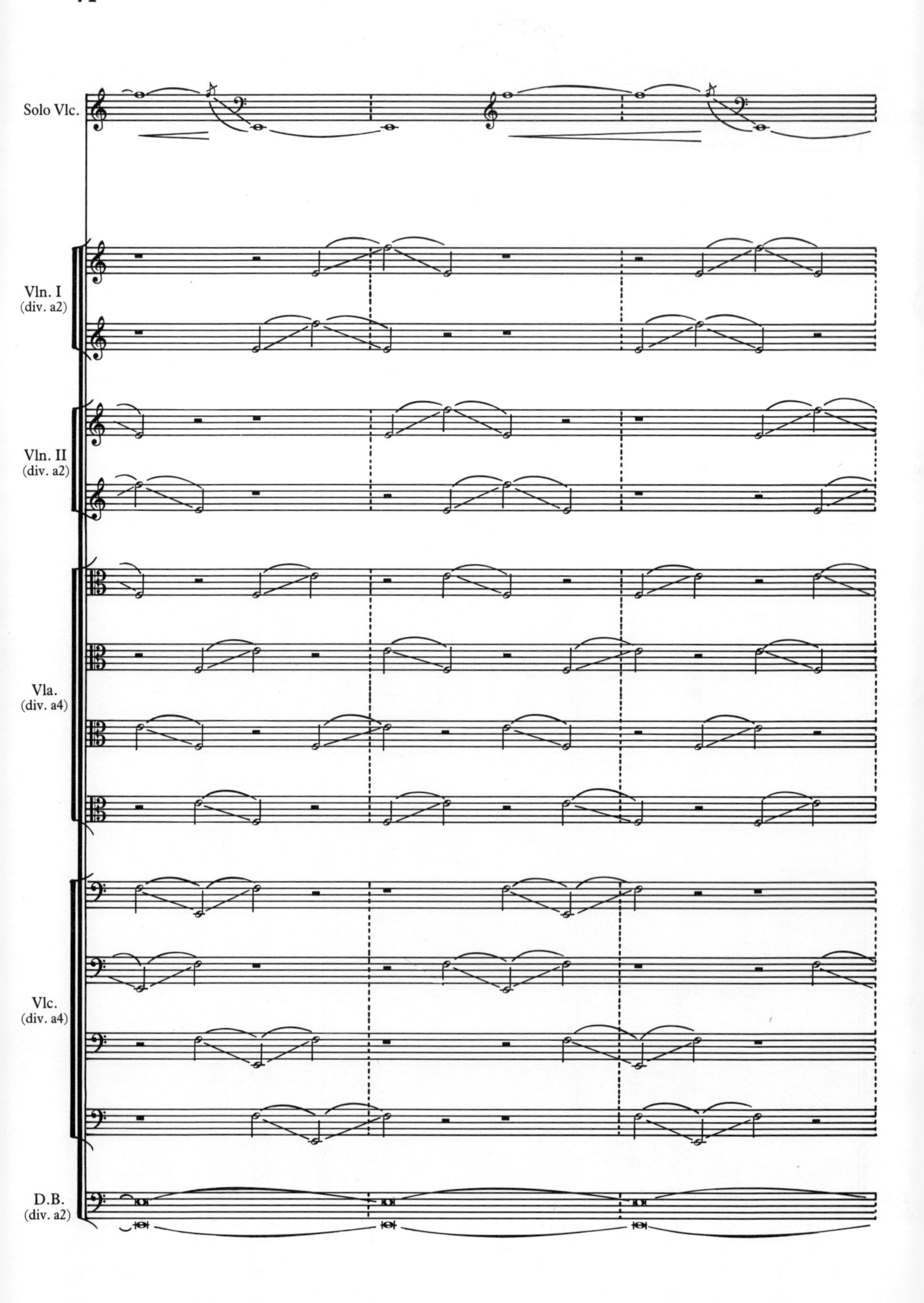

Solo Vlc.
Vln. I
(div. a2)
Vln. II
(div. a2)
Vla.
(div. a4)
Vlc.
(div. a4)
D.B.
(div. a2)

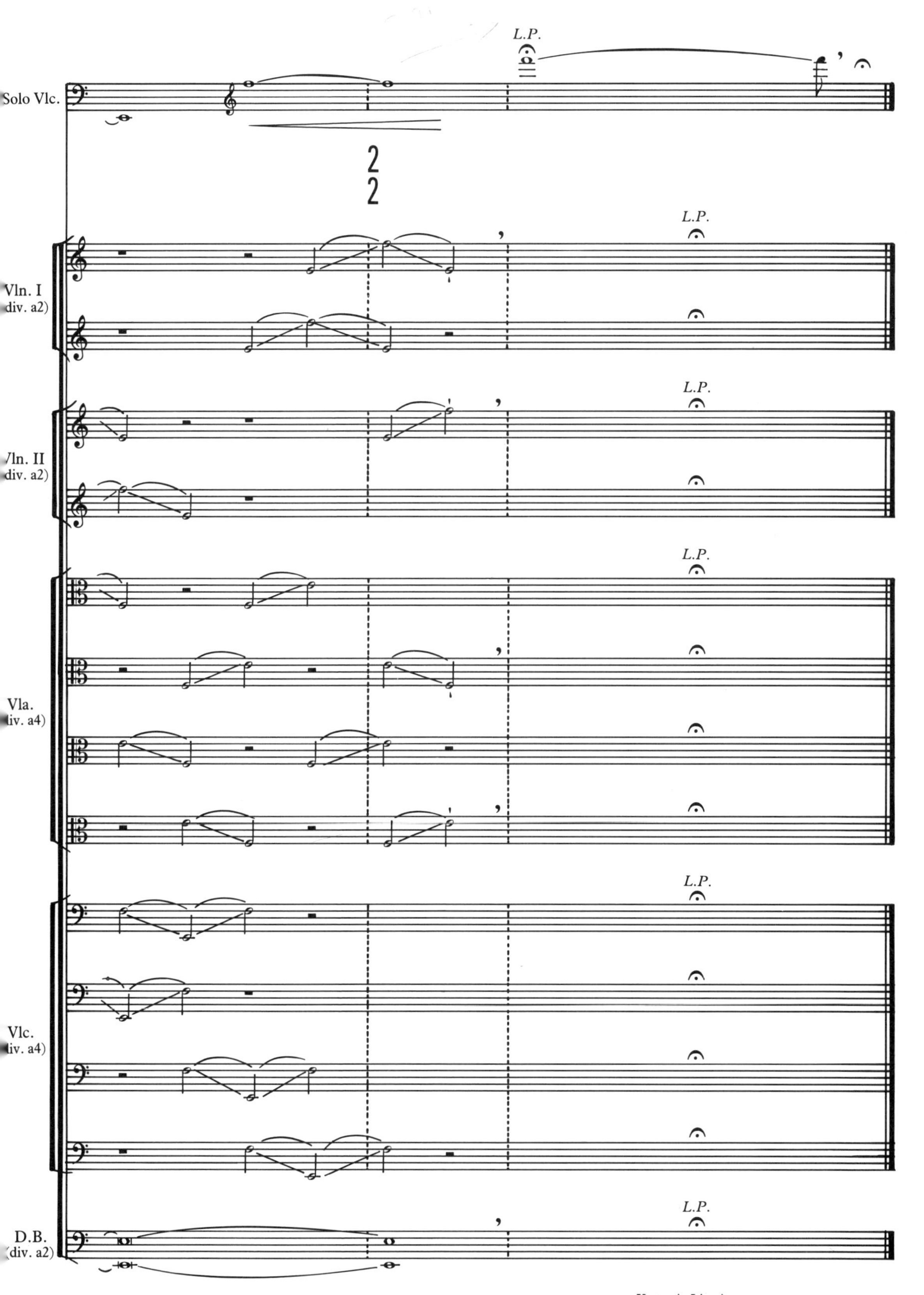

Katounia Limni
Eve of the Protecting Veil – 13th October 1987